The Surfer's Guide to Waves, Coasts and Climates

Tony Butt

Alison Hodge

To Anabel

Contents

Introduction

The empty wave

The surfer paddled out and looked at the empty wave. He had probably seen a thousand waves like this. Nevertheless, he remained there, awestruck by its beauty and symmetry. He thought about why that wave broke so perfectly. For good waves to appear, especially as big and perfect as this one, everything must be just right: the swell direction, the swell size and the wind conditions, plus the shape of the reef or sandbar over which the wave breaks. He thought about how clever Nature must be to produce something so special.

Then, he wondered how many factors must have gone into the making of that wave. To start with, the local geology of the area is what determines whether the wave will encounter a reef, sandbar, rivermouth or some other formation, when it hits the coast. And the exact shape of that formation is what decides the final shape of the wave – right, left, slow, fast, long, short, radical or mellow, or, indeed, whether it will be rideable at all. What's more, that wave didn't just appear at that spot; it was the result of a storm that was generated thousands of kilometres away. That storm might not have existed if the air flow in the upper part of the atmosphere had been different. And that air flow might not have been the same if the Northern hemisphere had been in a different phase of a long-term atmospheric cycle. The surfer realized that a wave breaking on a beach is a truly 'global' phenomenon, connected to many other things in faraway places and distant times. He had the feeling that, in some way, the entire planet had contributed to the formation of that humble wave.

He imagined what it would be like to be on that wave: to sense the speed; to see and hear the water rushing by; to smell and taste the ocean. He imagined himself jamming a big bottom turn, carving an arc under the lip, and throwing a rooster-tail of spray over the back of the wave. Then he imagined what it would be like for someone else, standing on the beach, watching him surfing that wave. He decided that that person would never be able to experience the wave in the same way as he would. His 'observation' of himself riding the wave

could never be the same as someone else's observation from a distance.

He thought about it for a little longer. The surfer – the person uniquely experiencing the sight, sound, taste and smell of that wave – is actually changing the form and the shape of the wave by being on it. The board is interfering with the water surface, making the wave break differently, and the surfer himself is altering the atmosphere around the wave.

If he had tried to 'experience' that empty wave by riding it, he would have changed it. It would no longer have been empty because it would have contained him, the surfer. Yet, changing the shape of an empty wave by riding it doesn't really damage the wave, or stop the surfer enjoying it. Normally, the act of riding a wave – of enjoying that particular natural phenomenon by experiencing it directly – is completely inoffensive, and has no serious knock-on effects. The only person who might possibly be affected is someone on the beach who wanted to watch an empty wave, instead of one with someone on it.

However, there are more extreme cases, where trying to enjoy something too much can result in that thing being damaged. There are cases where somebody thinks they have to seriously physically modify something in order to enjoy it. If that thing is a natural phenomenon like a wave or, indeed, the coast itself, there are always problems. If, for example, somebody wanted to 'enjoy the coast' a little more, and built a yacht harbour over the top of the sandbar where a good wave was breaking, it might destroy that surf spot all together, seriously affecting the lives of local surfers and local residents whose livelihood depends on surfing. There are other, more complicated, cases where trying to be too greedy and 'enjoy something too much' results not only in the loss of that thing, but also in a great deal of damage to some completely unrelated natural phenomenon. For example, somebody might want to enjoy the benefits of a lot of profit from buying and selling crude oil. If they don't sacrifice some of that profit to transport the oil safely, they might lose that oil, and also seriously pollute hundreds of kilometres of coastline.

In many cases, too much altering of the natural environment feeds right back to the perpetrators themselves. For example, the building of a yacht harbour in a sensitive area such as a rivermouth might cause unexpected coastal erosion a few kilometres down the coast, resulting in one of the yacht owners' own houses falling into the sea. Of course, things are not normally as clear-cut as that, and the connection cannot always be made by people. But if you look carefully, this kind of feedback happens everywhere, on every scale, right up to our most serious global problem at the moment: global warming. The fact that we are trying to 'enjoy' the Earth's natural resources too much means that we are using up those natural resources too quickly, polluting the atmosphere, and changing the climate. In other words, we are causing problems for ourselves. It seems that, if we abuse Nature too much, it will complain and bite back at us.

At one time, people thought that humans were special compared with other life forms on this planet. Fortunately, not many people subscribe to this arrogant view nowadays. We now know that we are no more 'special' than chimpanzees or giraffes, and that we evolved in the same way as an earthworm or a mosquito. The idea is simple: we, the animals and plants, gradually evolve, through the process of natural selection, to follow the gradual changes in the non-living parts of the planet, such as the rocks, the water and the air. Recently, however, scientists have realized that we shouldn't really separate the animals and plants from the rocks and water. Instead of us just evolving to follow the changes in our environment, our environment also evolves to follow the changes in us. In fact, everything on the planet evolves together – animals, plants, bacteria, oceans, atmosphere, mountains, deserts and coasts, all connected together by an infinite maze of feedback loops. The planet is a self-regulating super-organism, each element within it evolving in harmony with all the other elements.

What seems to be happening now, though, is that we humans are out of balance with everything else. Our effect on the other components of the planet is disproportionately high compared with the other components' effect on us. We seem recently to have stumbled upon the power to alter the environment more than the environment is altering us. By burning fossil fuels millions of times faster than they are being produced; by altering the composition of the atmosphere so that the Earth's temperature isn't being regulated properly, or by killing off our fellow species faster than new ones are emerging, we are seriously compromising the harmony between us and the other elements of the planet. We are making the mistake of trying to control Nature as if we were somehow more intelligent or more important, instead of realizing that we are simply just another part of it.

Not thinking we own Nature, and realizing we are a part of it, is a concept that we surfers should find a little easier to grasp than most people. Being 'part of Nature' is what we are doing when we surf a wave that has a long, long story behind it – a story involving the interconnection of a great many elements of our living planet.

The surfer sat and watched a few more waves from the channel. From this angle, you could really appreciate the beauty and symmetry of the waves. The water was teeming with life, and much colder than it looked. This was the upwelling, caused by a recent spell of strong cross-offshores, due to a big high-pressure system. Luckily, the beach was backed by a large pine forest – a perfect device for absorbing those winds and keeping the waves glassy. The forest also doubled up as his positional aid in the line-up – he could see the top of a distant mountain through a gap in the trees. He looked around him. He was already having the time of his life, and he hadn't even caught a wave yet.

What's in this book?

This book is about those aspects of Nature that I think you will be most interested in if you are a surfer: the waves, the coast and the climate, from a surfing point of view.

You will notice that the book is made up of four different sections, containing three chapters each. This is because the sections have enough autonomy for you to be able to read them in any order, or leave some of them out, if you want. Of course, it is better if you read all of them, and in the order in which they appear, since there is a common thread running through the whole book.

Each section really just gives a taster of the subject it covers, trying to keep it nice and simple, and relevant to surfing. I've tried not to make any of it incomprehensible to those of you without a background in science. To enjoy this book, all you need is curiosity, a love of the coast and the waves, and a little of that child-like wonder; but not a doctorate in physics. If you want to dig deeper into the subjects I have introduced, I have recommended a few books with more in-depth information (see pages 172–3).

This book is not a textbook. It is not a set of facts that you might need to know in order to pass some exam, get a job, earn more money, or become a better person. Neither is it me preaching my own ideas and telling you what you should and shouldn't be doing about global warming or environmental abuse, although those subjects do come up quite a bit. Mostly, I want you to use it as entertainment – something that you enjoy reading and will remember as a pleasant experience. But, also, I want the book to inspire your own thoughts on the subjects I have skimmed the surface of; and I want it to be something that might enhance your own experience of Nature and the coast by giving you a little more knowledge about what is going on.

Coastal Geology

Waves for surfing come in all different shapes and sizes. There are rights, lefts, peaks, slow waves, fast waves, big, small, long, short, sectiony, powerful, weak or hollow waves, to name but a few. There are many reasons why waves are so different from each other, but perhaps the most important reason is the shape of the platform upon which they break. The form of the sea bed underneath the waves, and the material it is made of, is what ultimately determines the shape of those waves as they break. So, in this section of the book I'm going to talk about wave-breaking platforms.

First, we take a look at beaches: those deceptively complex natural systems made up of millions upon millions of identical tiny grains, piled on top of each other and capable of morphing into an infinite variety of different shapes. The shape of the waves breaking on a beach is determined by the morphology of that beach, which, in turn, is controlled by the action of the waves themselves. This feedback loop is one thing that makes the study of beach morphology very difficult, but, at the same time, fascinating.

Then we move on to reefs. Unlike beaches, these platforms don't change their shape (at least on time-scales to which we can relate). However, they can still produce a bewildering array of different wave types. The ways in which reefs are formed couldn't be more varied either: from molten lava spewing out of the ground to pieces of the same lava, now solidified, falling from giant cliff tops, to grains of dust or the carcases of dead animals imperceptibly accumulating over millions of years.

Lastly, we look at rivermouths. Admittedly, rivermouth sandbars and the waves they produce could be classed as a sub-category among beachbreaks. However, these natural systems are at least as complicated as beaches, and just as difficult to study. The science of rivermouths is an intricate mix of physics, biology, chemistry and geology. The waves that break on them are of a special kind, too, including some of the most hollow and most perfect waves in the world.

1 Waves and beaches

Some people spend their entire lives surfing on reefs, but most of us also spend a great deal of time surfing on beaches. In this chapter I'm going to describe a few aspects of the behaviour of beaches that more or less directly affect the waves for surfing – or are readily noticeable by us. For our purposes we can define a beach, or beachbreak, as a wave-breaking platform whose material can be moved around by the waves themselves on a regular basis. Let's say the material includes any sediment up to about 30 cm in diameter. Larger rocks do move, of course, but much less frequently, so are not of any significance to us.

One important difference between beaches and reefs is that beaches have the ability to mutate in response to wave conditions, whereas reefs don't. With reefs, on a day-to-day basis at least, the connection between the waves and the sea floor is simple and one-way. A reef is a certain shape, so a given wave will break in a certain way. There is no 'feedback' between the waves and the reef. With beaches, the connection between the water and the sediment is more like a chicken-and-egg situation than a simple cause-and-effect relationship. The sea-floor topography – the *morphology* – affects the way the waves break, and the waves move the sediment to change the shape of the sea floor which, in turn, alters the way the waves break. There is a feedback loop between the sediment and water movement, which scientists are now trying to understand using chaos theory.

If you thought a beachbreak was a beachbreak, and that the waves that broke there were basically of one type, then you'd be mistaken. There is great variety in the shape and form of beaches, and the waves that break on them. Beaches can be vastly different according to their geographical position, orientation, composition and geological origins. Only a handful of the millions of beaches on this planet are suitable for surfing, and those that are suitable are by no means all the same.

So where do beaches come from? Beaches are principally made of grains of sediment derived from the disintegration of the land. The process that forms beaches is the reverse of that which forms sedimentary rocks. Instead of layer upon layer of sediment being trapped and compressed into solid rock, the sediment grains are 'set free' from existing rocks, effectively undoing the original sedimentation mechanism. In tropical areas where the sea is teaming with life, many beaches also contain a large amount of material derived from shells and skeletons of dead animals.

The ways in which the sediment got on to the shoreline are various. For example, it may have been eroded directly from local rocks by the action of the waves themselves, or it may have been eroded from other rocks some distance along the coast and then carried by an alongshore current; or it may have reached the coast from the outflow of a river. Whatever material the beach is made of, and wherever it came from, it only stays put if the prevailing wave, current and tidal conditions are just right. If the waves and currents are such that a particular type of sediment is likely to get washed away, then it will get washed away. As a result, the form and composition of every beach reflects not only the type of beach-making material (rock or biological material) generally common in that area, but also the prevailing hydrodynamic conditions along that stretch of coast.

Why are some beaches steeper than others?

One notable difference between beaches is that some are steeper than others. This affects the waves that break on them, and the characteristics of those waves for surfing. Generally, the rule is that steeper beaches have steeper waves, and flatter beaches have flatter waves. On steeper beaches, the sudden depth change makes the waves break more suddenly, and dissipate their energy more quickly. On flatter beaches, with their more gradual depth change, the waves break more gently, because the energy is dissipated more slowly over a greater distance. On the very steepest beaches the waves don't even break – they just surge up and down; and on the very flattest beaches the waves can be disappointingly slow – breaking a long way out with little power. Either extreme is of limited use for surfing.

You may have noticed, although it is not always the case, that steeper beaches have larger grain sizes. Beaches made of large stones are very often the steepest, rarely containing good surfing waves (unless, of course, there is some reef nearby). Willard Bascom couldn't help but notice the possible relationship between grain size and beach steepness. In 1951 he did some experiments at Half-moon Bay, California, and confirmed with his results that large-grained beaches do tend to be steeper than small-grained beaches. Half-moon Bay was then completely unknown in the embryonic world of international surfing. Nevertheless, Bascom surely must have been aware of surfing, even in 1951, since it was already thriving in California. I wonder if he ever looked out towards Pillar Point during his experiments, and if he possibly imagined what would be going on there 50 or 60 years later?

The widely accepted reason as to why large-grained beaches tend to be steeper has to do with *percolation* – or the sinking of water into the sediment. Right at the shoreline of any beach, regardless of where the waves break, there is always an area where the water just swashes up and down. This is the *swash zone*. The part of the cycle where the water rushes up the beach is called the *uprush*, and the part where the water rushes back again is called the *backwash*. The uprush is like a tongue of water spreading up a dry beach. Sometimes, if you stare at the shoreline, it seems like the water just keeps coming shoreward in tongues and tongues, without ever flowing back again. You wonder where all that water is going, until you realize it is sinking into the sand. Since beach sediment is porous, the water of the uprush tends to sink into the beach, filtering, or percolating, its way through the grains. If much of the water from the uprush is lost in this way, there won't be any left for the backwash.

Since sediment on beaches is moved principally by the action of the water 'rubbing' along the bottom and scooping up the sediment, any imbalance between uprush and backwash is reflected in an imbalance in the movement of sediment on that part of the beach. If the uprush flow is stronger than the backwash flow (because the backwash has been lost due to percolation), there will be a preferential transport of sediment in the direction of the uprush (towards the shore). The sediment will then start to pile up, making the beach steeper and steeper.

Of course, the sediment cannot keep piling up for ever, so there must be some other force that stops the beach steepening once it reaches a certain point. That force is gravity. As the beach gets steeper and steeper, the effect of gravity on the flow becomes progressively greater, the uprush struggling more and more to climb up a steeper slope, and the backwash having an easier and easier ride back downhill. As the beach gets steeper, the uprush becomes weaker and the backwash stronger. This effect is exactly opposite to that produced by percolation, so, eventually, a point is reached where the two cancel each other out. The uprush and backwash flows are once again equal, and the beach stops steepening. It has reached a point of dynamic equilibrium, as shown in the diagram.

Now, here is the crucial part. A beach made of bigger grains lets more water sink into it than one made of smaller grains. In other words, bigger grains mean more percolation. Therefore, on coarse-grained beaches, more of the backwash is lost, and the imbalance brought about by percolation is larger than that on fine-grained beaches. The beach has to steepen much more in order for gravity to compensate (i.e., large grains = more percolation = more gravity = steeper beach). In contrast, fine-grained beaches do not allow much percolation, so they do not have to steepen very much before equilibrium between gravity and percolation is reached. The overall result is exactly what is commonly observed: that coarse-grained beaches are steeper than fine-grained ones.

After the work of Bascom, a few other scientists performed similar experiments on similar beaches, and plotted similar graphs. The data they came up with followed the same trends as those of Bascom. However, on comparing their graphs with his, it became apparent that the steepness of a beach also depends on the characteristics of the incoming waves. The beaches tending to receive smaller wave heights had steeper slopes, and those receiving larger wave heights had flatter slopes. This is logical, since

(1) Percolation of water into the sand inhibits the offshore flow of water.

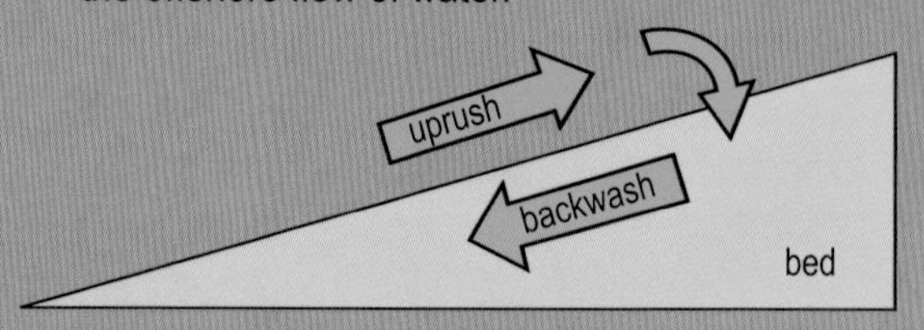

(2) The uprush above the bed builds up the sediment and steepens the beach.

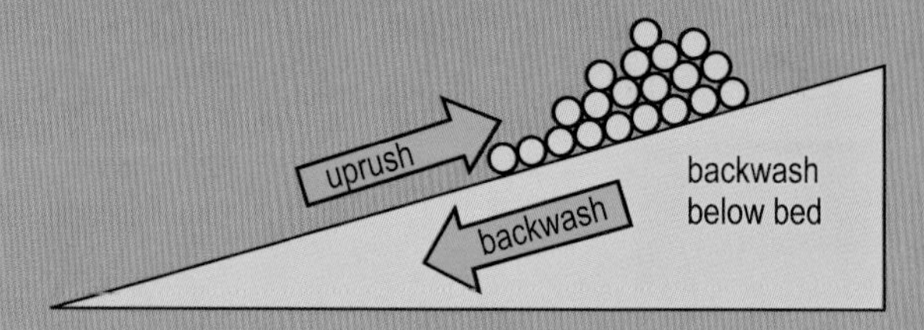

(3) As the beach steepens, gravity enhances the backwash until the beach stops steepening.

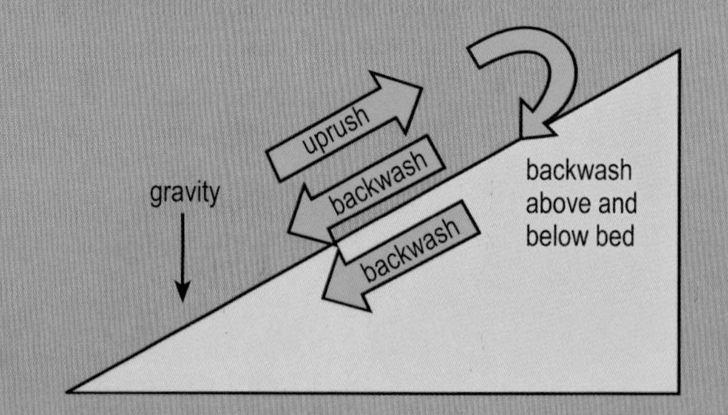

(1) Percolation of water into the sand inhibits the offshore flow of water in the swash zone, allowing the stronger onshore flow to keep building up sediment on the shore and steepening the beach. (2) As the beach gets steeper and steeper, the enhancement of the offshore flow and the impediment of the onshore flow due to gravity begin to compensate for the percolation. (3) Once a point is reached where the onshore and offshore flows above the bed are equal, the beach stops getting steeper.

An uprush tongue licks its way up a dry beach.

we also know that big storms tend to cause coastal erosion leading to a flattening of the beach, and small waves cause accretion which tends to steepen the beach.

Reflective and dissipative beaches

In fact, steep and not-so-steep beaches have a whole host of interesting differences in the way they respond to different wave conditions. These have been classified and quantified by the experts, allowing them to predict how a beach will behave according to the existing morphology and current wave conditions, and the history of both.

Extremely gently sloping beaches are known as *dissipative* beaches. This is because the waves break a long way outside, from where they slowly roll in, continually losing energy until they reach the shore. The wave energy at the shoreline of a dissipative beach – typically measured by the intensity of the uprush-backwash movements – is much less than the wave energy at the breakpoint. The wide, shallow area that the broken waves have to propagate across dissipates most of that energy. If the wave height suddenly increases on a dissipative beach, then the waves simply start breaking further out. The extra wave energy due to their increased height is then dissipated over the extra distance from the breakpoint to the shore. As a result, the extra energy does not 'register' at the shoreline. The waves still reach the shore having lost almost all their energy, no matter how big they were when they broke.

Really steep beaches are known as *reflective* beaches. Here the waves dump very close to the shore, either as 'plunging' waves or, in extreme cases, as 'surging' waves. Surging waves do not actually break; they just surge up and down the beach. The wave energy at the breakpoint is transmitted directly to the shore because there is not enough distance between the breakpoint and the shore to dissipate it. Sometimes the waves reflect off the steep beach in the form of backwash – hence the term 'reflective'. If the wave height increases on a reflective beach, the waves won't break much further out. The energy on the shoreline will increase in direct proportion to the breaking wave height. In contrast to a dissipative beach, any variations in wave height are reproduced faithfully as corresponding variations in uprush-backwash motions at the shoreline.

Now, I am going to eat my words. I have just stated that, on a dissipative beach, the energy of the waves is used up between the breakpoint and the shore. However, not *all* the energy is used up. The *incident waves* – those we surf – are definitely dissipated; but there are other, mysterious, long-period waves called *infragravity waves* – unseen and embedded within the normal waves – which do in fact manage to get through. Our understanding of infragravity waves is still quite poor, so I won't say much about them. What we do know is that 'something happens' between the breakpoint and the shore to make these infragravity waves appear, particularly in dissipative conditions. When the surf is big on a highly dissipative beach, you can quite easily see the whole shoreline moving backwards and forwards in long, slow motions. These are the infragravity waves in action. Sometimes, you can see three or four lines of whitewater coming in, stacked one on top of the other. Then the water suddenly draws back hundreds of metres. That is the uprush and backwash of an infragravity wave. Because infragravity waves have a much longer wavelength than normal waves, they never break, even on the most gently sloping beaches. From the point of view of an infragravity wave, any beach is a steep beach. So, no matter what the beach, infragravity waves remain unbroken, and maintain their energy all the way through to the shoreline. Any increase in wave height on a dissipative beach *will* result in an increase in the intensity of uprush-backwash motions, but only for the infragravity waves. In summary, if the wave height increases on a dissipative beach, there will be more and more stacking up of lines of whitewater, followed by those huge, long drawbacks. This is shown in the diagram.

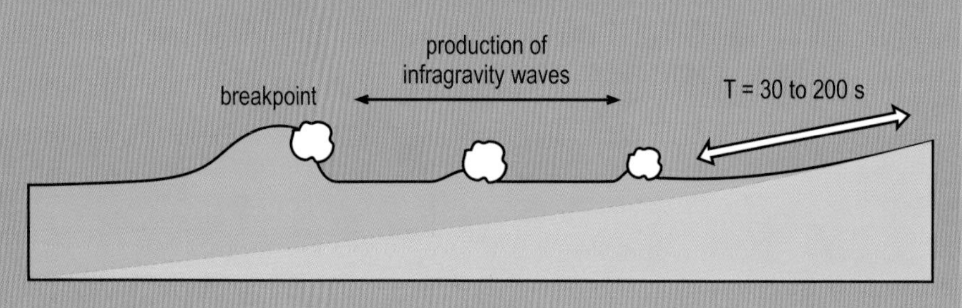

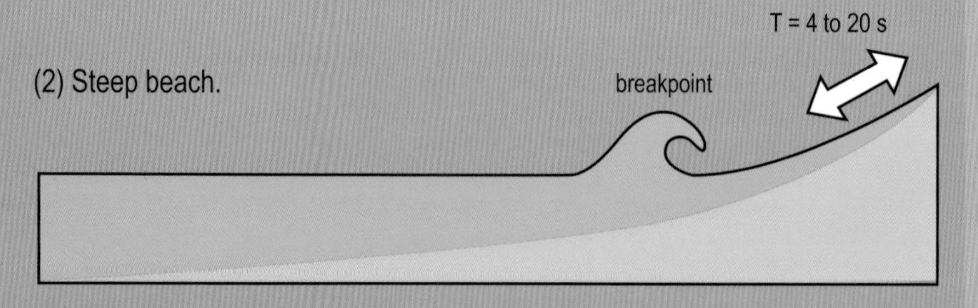

(1) On a gently sloping beach, the waves break a long way out, dissipating almost all their energy before they reach the shore. The shoreline moves in and out in long, slow motions (wave periods [T] of between about 30 and 200 seconds [s]) in tune with the infragravity waves, which keep all their energy right up to the shore. (2) On a steep beach, the waves break closer to the shore, and all the energy is transmitted through to the shoreline. The shoreline moves in and out at the same frequency as the waves themselves (periods of between about 4 and 20 seconds).

On steep, reflective beaches the majority of the wave energy is felt right up to the shoreline.

A classification system that identifies all the characteristics of dissipative, reflective, and about four sub-categories of intermediate beaches was developed in 1983 by Australian scientists Don Wright and Andy Short. Their study was based on a huge number of beaches around the coast of Australia. In addition to illustrations showing the various features of each type of beach, they produced simple formulae based on wave height, period and beach slope, to determine whereabouts a beach might lie in the dissipative-reflective continuum. A beach tends towards dissipative if it has a gentle slope and big waves with short periods. The waves break further out, not only because of the relatively flat beach, but also because bigger, shorter-period waves are steeper, and therefore 'trip up' and break more easily. In contrast, a beach with a steep slope and small waves with long periods tends towards reflective. Here, the waves break closer to the shore, not only because of the steep slope, but also because smaller, longer-period waves won't steepen up and break until they come into much shallower water (see diagram on page 18).

Of course, the values of wave height, period and beach slope that put certain beaches into dissipative, intermediate or reflective categories are only *typical* values found on that beach. They determine whereabouts in the continuum that beach is likely to be most of the time, but they are not fixed for each beach. Some beaches, especially those that receive a wide range of wave heights and periods, might move between reflective and intermediate, or between intermediate and dissipative, depending on the conditions.

Surfing on either extreme of dissipative or reflective beaches is generally not as good as on those beaches that lie somewhere in between. Extremely reflective beaches are practically unsurfable, especially if they are so steep that the waves just surge up and down. But on highly dissipative beaches, you might have to punch your way through line after line of whitewater, only to find the waves lacking any kind of power once you get out the back. Beaches that lie in between the dissipative and reflective ends of the continuum are known as *intermediate* beaches. These are generally the best beaches for surfing. For one thing, the beach slope is just right for the waves to have a reasonable amount of power but not to break so close to the shore that they become impossible shore dumpers.

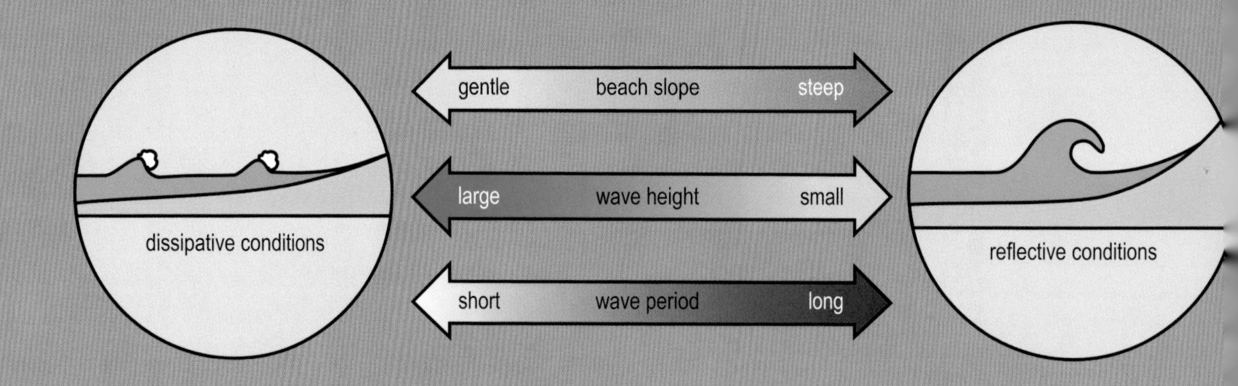

Not only the beach slope, but also the height and period of the incoming waves govern whether conditions will end up being dissipative, reflective, or somewhere in between the two.

Also, intermediate beaches are usually the ones that contain good sandbars for surfing. The shape and position of the sandbars are obviously crucial for deciding how the waves will break for surfing.

Sandbars and feedback

The quality of the surf on a reef or beachbreak depends upon many factors, mostly to do with the swell, wind and tide. But the quality of surf on a beachbreak depends upon one extra factor: the sandbars. As I mentioned at the beginning of this chapter, the fact that the sea floor of a reef is fixed and the sea floor of a beach is movable, represents a fundamental difference between the two. On a beachbreak, the waves won't be right unless the sandbars are right – even if everything else is perfect.

Whether or not there are good sandbars for surfing depends upon the way in which the waves act on the beach to modify its shape, plus the way in which the beach itself acts on the waves to modify the way they break. This is a classic feedback loop. Normally, if the incoming wave conditions remain stable for long enough, the system reaches a state of equilibrium and the beach morphology is also stable. However, if the wave conditions suddenly change, so does the morphology. The morphology then feeds back to change the shape of the waves, which, in turn, change the morphology in a slightly different way. This to-and-fro behaviour goes on for a while until the beach settles down to a new state of equilibrium. The sandbars that were there before are now a different shape, or have moved to a different place. In a system like this, the morphology and the waves are always playing cat and mouse. The waves, essentially being the 'input' to the system, are the first to change. Once this happens, the system is thrown out of equilibrium for a while until the morphology readjusts itself to the new wave conditions. This won't happen instantly: the time taken for any changes to filter through – the *response time* of the system – could be a matter of hours or days.

So, how exactly do the waves affect the beach morphology, and how does the beach morphology feed back to affect the waves? This is a complicated question, but we can throw a little light on it by using a simple conceptual model called the *breakpoint-bar hypothesis* (see diagram on page 19). This is a nice, easy explanation, using the feedback idea mentioned above, of how a sandbar forms under the breaking waves. The breakpoint-bar hypothesis explains how, offshore of the breakpoint, there is movement of sediment towards the beach and, onshore of the breakpoint, there

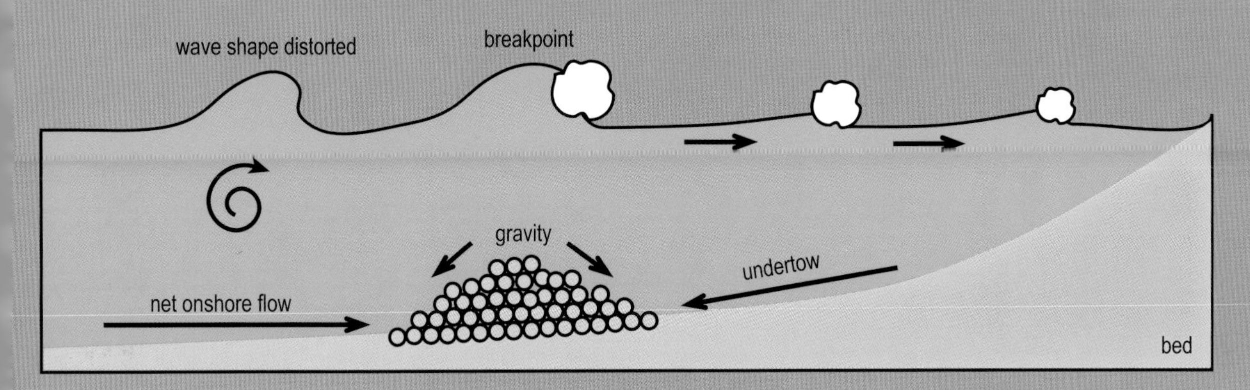

The breakpoint-bar hypothesis. The onshore movement of water seaward of the breakpoint due to Stokes drift, and the offshore movement of water landward of the breakpoint due to the undertow, maintain the bar in position. Once the bar builds up to a certain level, gravity stops it building up any more by making the grains roll back down again. (In the diagram, the beach appears much steeper than it would be in real life.)

is movement of sediment away from the beach. This means that the sediment tends to accumulate at the breakpoint itself.

The onshore sediment movement beyond the breakpoint stems from a phenomenon called *Stokes drift*. Stokes drift is the steady movement of water towards the shore just beyond the breakpoint. It comes about because, as the waves move into shallow water, the interaction between the waves and the sea bed distorts the waves. They take on a 'pitched-forward' profile, as if poised to topple over and break. Without this distortion, the water right next to the bed would just move backwards and forwards by the same amount. However, with the wave distorted like this, the near-bed water movement is stronger in the onshore than in the offshore direction. This results in a net onshore movement of water, and, therefore, the sediment that the water drags with it.

Likewise, shorewards of the breakpoint, there is a net drift of water under the waves in an offshore direction. This comes about because the water driven towards the beach on the surface by the whitewater must somehow return towards the sea. One mechanism that allows this to happen is called *undertow* – where the water that is brought onshore on the surface returns offshore beneath the surface, under the breaking waves. This offshore-flowing water drags sediment with it, towards the breakpoint.

The system is self-reinforcing, first because the distortion of the waves before they break becomes more pronounced as the sandbar builds up. This means more shoreward movement of water, and more sand being dragged towards the breakpoint from the outside. Second, as the sandbar builds up, the waves break with more force. So the amount of water carried towards the shore on the surface by the broken waves is greater, which means more water returning in the undertow, and more sand being dragged towards the breakpoint from the inside.

If this process continued, the sandbar would keep building up and building up for ever. It doesn't, which means there must be something that stops it. There must be some mechanism that comes into play at some point to suppress the feedback loop I've just described. Once again, it's gravity. As soon as the bar has built up to a certain level of steepness, gravity starts to make the grains roll back down again. When the 'building-up' action of the water motion exactly balances the 'rolling-down' action due to gravity, the bar reaches a state of equilibrium and will not build up any more.

A classic sandbar system, seen at low tide.

The *summer-winter profile* is one of the simplest examples of the breakpoint-bar hypothesis in action. Here, the on-offshore movement of sediment makes the shape of the beach change from one season to another. In summer, the waves are generally small, and so tend to break in relatively shallow water, fairly close to the shore. According to the breakpoint-bar hypothesis, the sand accumulates under the breakpoint close to the shore, or right on it. The summer profile therefore contains a steep bank or *berm* on the shore or a sandbar a few metres outside. In the winter, however, the waves tend to be bigger and to break in deeper water, which means that, by the same reasoning, a sandbar forms much further out, perhaps hundreds of metres from the shore. It has been suggested that the winter profile is a natural protection mechanism against shoreline erosion, since it forces the bigger waves to dissipate their energy quite a long way offshore. Without this 'protection', winter storms would have a much more profound effect on property built near the coast.

Stokes drift
bar
channel
rip
undertow
shoreline

A bar-channel system. White arrows = surface flow; black arrows = flow near the bed; blue arrows = flow at all depths. The sandbars are maintained in place by the feedback between the water motions and the shape of the sandbars themselves. Good, stable sandbars mean good, stable surfing waves.

Good sandbars for surfing

The breakpoint bar hypothesis only describes how a sandbar is formed from onshore and offshore sediment transport and, therefore, only views the sandbar as a two-dimensional object. In other words, it doesn't consider any variations in morphology along the shore – in the *alongshore* direction – and assumes all sandbars to be like giant sausages stretching the entire length of a beach. The waves too would be uniform in the alongshore direction: in other words, they would close out. This is often seen on small 'pocket' beaches, but is rare (although not impossible) on long stretches of straight coastline. Here, there is usually a sandbar 'system' consisting of a series of lumps and dips – the waves breaking on the lumps but not in the dips.

The formation of these lumps and dips involves alongshore transport of sediment as well as on-offshore transport. Alongshore transport can sometimes be a secondary consequence of on-offshore transport. Imagine, for example, that a sandbar starts off with only very slight, random variations in height in the alongshore direction. The incoming waves would focus, or bend, ever so slightly, towards the lumps and away from the dips. They might then start to break on the lumps but not on the dips. The breakpoint-bar mechanism would then immediately come into play, causing sand to preferentially accumulate under the breakpoint. This would effectively reinforce the lumps, which would also enhance the focusing effect and make the waves break more strongly, which, according to the breakpoint-bar hypothesis, would make the undertow stronger. Again, a feedback mechanism is created. Now, in addition to the undertow, the water brought onshore by the breaking waves also finds its way back out to sea via rip currents (see diagram on page 20). These first flow away to the side of the breaking waves, and then out to sea in the channels where the original dips were. The rips help to maintain the lumps and dips by scooping up sediment in the channels and dumping it out just beyond the breakpoint. Meanwhile, the waves, instead of closing out, start to break as a series of peaks – much better for surfing than the close-outs you might find on a sausage-shaped, two-dimensional sandbar.

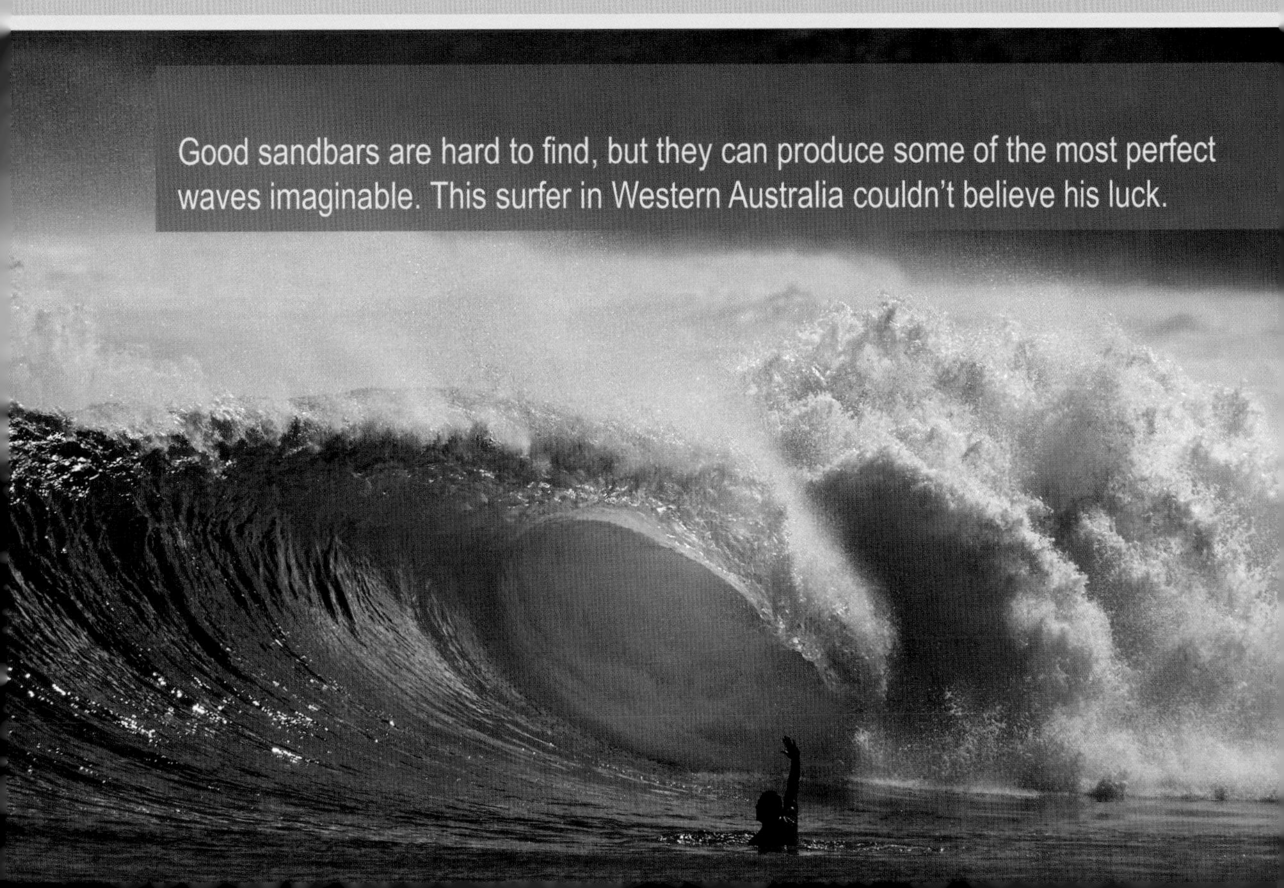
Good sandbars are hard to find, but they can produce some of the most perfect waves imaginable. This surfer in Western Australia couldn't believe his luck.

2 Reefs

When I first started surfing, at the age of ten, I thought every wave was more or less the same. I knew waves could be bigger or smaller, and I knew they could go left or right, but that was about all. And since the only waves I had ever seen were those breaking at my local beach, I thought all surfing waves broke on soft-sand beaches. It took me a little while to realize that another type of surf spot existed apart from the beachbreak: the reefbreak. I then started to suspect that, since beaches and reefs were made of different types of material, the way a wave broke on a beach was somehow different from the way it broke on a reef. Then, a few years later, I gradually began to realize that there wasn't just one type of reefbreak; they actually came in a vast variety of shapes and forms, depending on where you are in the world and what sort of coastal geology happens to be prevalent there.

In this chapter we are going to look at six different kinds of reefbreaks, their origins and physical characteristics, and how these affect the waves that break on them for surfing. When I say 'reefbreaks' I mean wave-breaking platforms made of immovable sea-floor material, which ranges from rock fixed to the land, to fairly large boulders that do not move even with the biggest storms. It also includes coral that started life on some fixed substrate such as an island or continental shelf. The six different categories of reef described are: *sedimentary-flat*, *sedimentary-folded*, *volcanic*, *fajãs*, *coral* and *granite*. Each one of these has its own particular set of features which affects the breaking waves in a variety of different ways.

Sedimentary-flat reefs

Sedimentary-flat reefs consist of flat, rocky platforms that stick out from the land into the sea in various shapes and sizes. Depending on the type of rock, these reefs are characterized by either rectangular blocks or flatter plates overlaying each other. In most cases, sharp, vertical variations in the height of the reef are relatively small – often less than a metre – which is a great advantage for surfing. The fact that the rock strata are almost horizontal indicates that the area in question has not been subject to any deformation or bending since the rock was formed (unlike 'sedimentary-folded' reefs, described below).

The material these reefs are made of is called sedimentary rock, which was formed by the gradual deposition of sediment over millions of years, layer upon layer. The grains of sediment that go to make up this kind of rock are originally carried along in some fluid (for example, water, air or ice). To maintain the sediment in suspension, the fluid has to be travelling above a particular threshold velocity. Above this velocity the turbulence in the fluid stops the grains being pulled down by gravity. If the speed of the fluid drops below this threshold, the turbulence is no longer strong enough to resist the force of gravity, and the sediment 'drops out' and finally ends up settling on the floor. Over time, many layers of sediment are deposited in this way. Eventually, after many thousands or millions of years, the layers at the bottom become squashed by the weight of all those successive layers. As a result, each layer is progressively converted into solid rock, from the bottom upwards.

Sedimentary rock is roughly categorized according to the size of the sediment that produced it. For example (from large to small): conglomerate, sandstone, silt, mudstone and limestone. Alternate layers of different sediment correspond to different periods through history, when different types of rock happened to prevail.

Many of the reefs in Western Australia are of the sedimentary-flat type.

For surfing, sedimentary-flat reefs have a whole host of advantages. Their relative evenness means that, apart from a few exceptions, getting in and out of the water is usually free of the complications often found with sedimentary-folded reefs or *fajãs*. You might get pounded on the bottom after going over the falls, but you'll be less likely to injure yourself than on some reef with sharp rocks sticking out of the water. Also, on these reefs, rideable waves are not restricted to a minimum or maximum size, nor are they restricted to a particular shape. In other words, depending on the orientation of the reef relative to the swell direction, along with the width of the reef and the angle of inclination into deep water, they can produce long, point-type waves; short, snappy barrels, or wedging A-frames.

One disadvantage of these reefs is that their natural formation does not always produce good waves for surfing. Along a typical stretch of coast containing sedimentary-flat reefs, you might find one or two classic spots; but there might also be many kilometres where the waves are frustratingly almost-surfable – closing out, backing off or doubling up. This is because, unlike volcanic reefs, *fajãs* or coral, the physical processes that form sedimentary-flat reefs do not automatically result in those reefs being natural shapes for good surfing waves to break on.

Sedimentary-folded reefs

Sedimentary-folded reefs are essentially the same as sedimentary-flat reefs, but with the difference that the rock strata are not necessarily horizontal. In the geographical area where the reef was formed, the strata may have been folded over at any angle up to and beyond 90°. As a result, the layers of rock that make up the reef can end up presenting themselves edge-on to the breaking waves. The reef may take the form of a series of rows of rock jutting out at right angles to the coast, sometimes highly visible

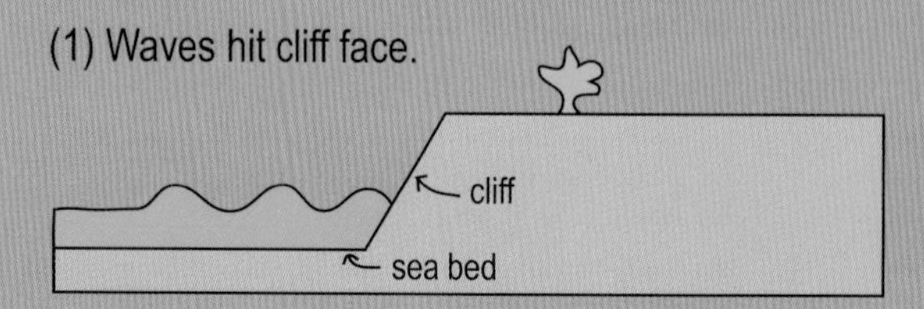

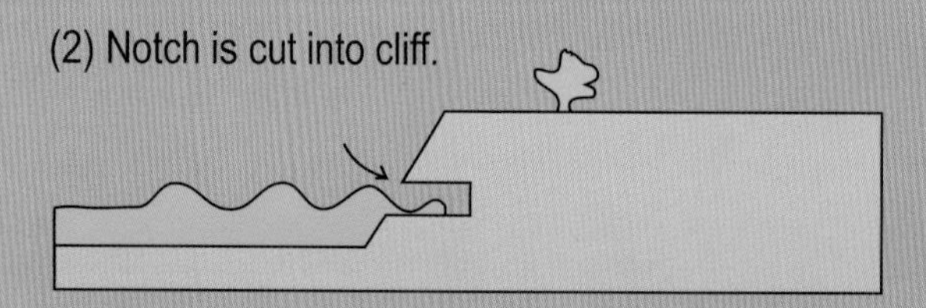

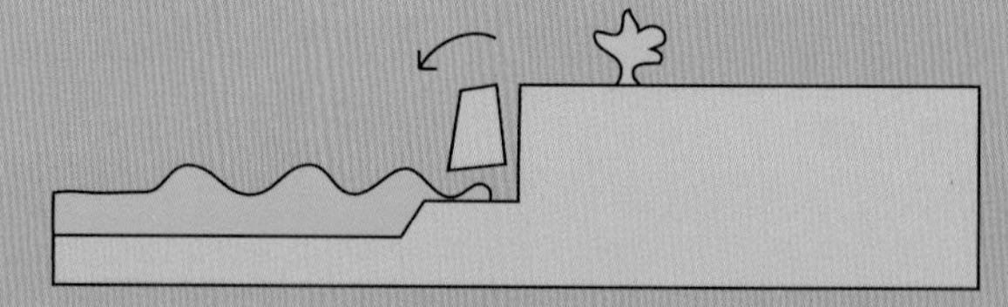

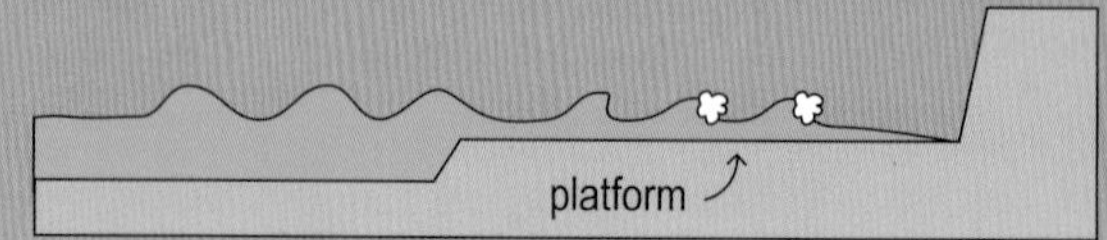

The formation of a wave-cut bench. (1) Unbroken waves crash into the cliff face. (2) The waves begin to cut a notch into the base of the cliff. (3) Rocky material above the notch falls into the sea and is washed away. (4) A platform is eventually formed upon which the waves can break.

A sedimentary-folded reef, typical of those found along the north coast of Spain.

at low tide. The surface of the reef is often extremely uneven and dangerous.

These reefs started life just like the horizontally stratified type described above, with the layers originally being formed by the gradual deposition of sediments. Then, some sudden geological event, such as a continental collision, caused the strata to bend over. I say 'sudden' but, of course, the event may have taken many thousands of years to happen. What is important is that it happens over a time-scale considerably shorter than that of the formation of the rock itself. An event of this kind happened in Europe about 55 million years ago, when the entire Iberian peninsula (containing what is now Spain and Portugal) rotated about 30° anticlockwise. This resulted in the formation of a huge wrinkle in the surface rock, along the axis of rotation, now known as the Pyrenees mountain range. The coastal cliffs and platforms of northern Spain are also folded over as a result of this event. You can see clearly the deformation patterns in the cliffs from the line-up at many spots along that coast.

Reefs made of sedimentary rock can often be found at the bottom of cliffs. A rock platform below a cliff is known by geologists as a 'wave-cut bench' (see diagram on page 24). The idea is that the cliff is gradually being eroded away by a continuing process. First, the action of the waves cuts a notch in the bottom of the cliff; then the part of the cliff above the notch starts to become unstable and falls into the sea. Most of the sediment that falls down gets washed away by wave action. Finally, what remains is a platform at the bottom of the cliff, just below the water surface. Note that, if a large number of hard boulders remain at the bottom of the cliff, then a *fajã* will begin to develop (see below).

Sedimentary-folded reefs can produce excellent waves. However, there are one or two disadvantages. The most obvious is that, in some spots, particularly where the rock strata have been folded over 90°, the platform over which you are surfing is highly uneven. The characteristics of the waves themselves are practically the same as those on the flatter reefs described above, but the minimum surfable wave height is usually bigger, due to the reef's unevenness. For example, at small sizes, you might find the best tube section occurs just where a nasty rock sticks out of the face of the wave. At some spots, the lines of rock look like giant saws or immense rows of shark's teeth. At others, considerable erosion has caused them to be flatter and less dangerous. The unevenness of the reef depends, to a certain extent, on the difference in the way adjacent layers of rock are eroded away. If the adjacent layers are of similar consistency, the reef will be eroded fairly evenly and will end up quite flat. Conversely, if the original strata consist of alternating soft and hard rock, then the waves will erode away the soft layers but not the hard ones. This will leave the hard layers to stick up like giant knives. Lastly, many of these spots have a safe, deep-water channel or a nearby beachbreak, but if they don't, getting in and out of the water can require a lot of studying beforehand.

Volcanic reefs

There is no doubt that volcanic rock tends to produce some of the best surfing reefs in the world. The reefs are formed from molten rock (lava or magma) flowing down from a volcano to the sea and cooling there. The treacle-like consistency of the lava, combined with the time it takes to solidify, means that the reefs tend to take the shape of giant tongues reaching out into the sea. Because they were once liquid, they tend to have surfaces with very little unevenness apart from a few pits and holes – a major advantage for surfing. The rock itself is a hard, black substance called basalt, sharp and rough in texture.

Gradjagan, Indonesia – one of the finest reefbreaks in the world.

Most volcanic reefs can be found on oceanic archipelagos such as Hawaii or the Canary Islands. The islands themselves are formed by magma that surges up from the asthenosphere, a zone lying between about 100 and 350 km below the Earth's surface. The temperature of the magma is normally about 1,300° C, but there are some anomalous regions where it reaches temperatures almost twice as high. It is at these 'hot spots' that the magma escapes to the outside world in the form of volcanoes. Some volcanic islands are formed at these hot spots, examples being Hawaii and the Canary Islands. However, some volcanic islands are formed at mid-ocean ridges. This is where two tectonic plates are drifting apart, allowing magma to rise up and escape through the gap. In the Atlantic Ocean, the islands of Ascension, the Azores and Iceland were

formed along the Mid-Atlantic Ridge. Volcanic material is coming out of the ground all the time and, occasionally, entire new islands are formed quite suddenly. For example, between 8 and 15 November 1963, the island of Surtsey, near Iceland, was formed. The volcano grew from the sea floor up to sea level (a distance of 130 m) in just one week.

The very nature of the physical processes that form volcanic reefs means that their shape is excellent for surfing. The tongue-like contours, produced when lava flows down from a volcano into the sea, can form a series of excellent rights and lefts along a short stretch of coast. The fact that these 'tongues' are found in a great number of different sizes means that an extensive range of wave heights is accommodated by this kind of reef. In Hawaii, for example, you can find 0.5–10 m-high surfable waves, all on volcanic lava reefs. Another, more indirect advantage, is that many volcanic reefs exist in zones where swell conditions are generally good. Volcanic islands with no continental shelf receive unhindered swells from a range of directions. If the islands are situated away from the mid-latitude storm belt (the area between about 30° and 60° latitude, where most low pressures develop), the swells will come in clean and lined-up.

Fajã reefs tend to form at the base of huge vertical cliffs, often making classic waves like this one inaccessible.

There are a few surfing disadvantages to volcanic reefs, but these hardly outweigh the advantages. One problem is that volcanic rock can be very sharp, so walking out over the reef or wiping out can mean cuts and grazes. Also, the rock tends to contain pits and holes, which can be dangerous in themselves if large enough. Lastly, volcanic reefs are often infested with urchins.

(1) Rocks fall into sea.
cliff
sea bed

Fajãs

Fajã is a Portuguese word meaning 'low, flat ground'. As far as reefs for surfing are concerned, *fajãs* are relatively narrow platforms produced by large rocks or boulders that have fallen down from a cliff or high coastal ground. The rocks are continually falling down and, as they accumulate at the bottom of the cliff, they are acted upon by the waves and currents, as shown in the diagram. These tend to wash away the smaller rocks and stones almost immediately, carrying them out to sea or along the coast. The larger, heavier rocks, however, tend to stay put, and are only moved very slightly by the waves, gradually adjusting their position over long periods of time. In fact, the shape of a *fajã* is usually the result of a state of equilibrium between the long-term average hydrodynamic conditions (the long-term behaviour of the waves and currents in that area) and the rate of supply of new rocks from the cliff.

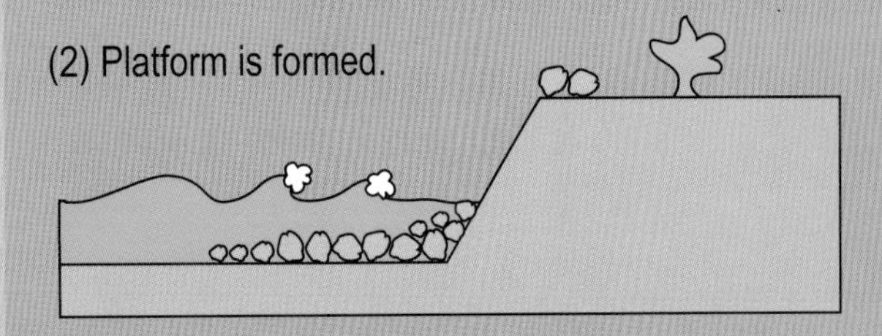

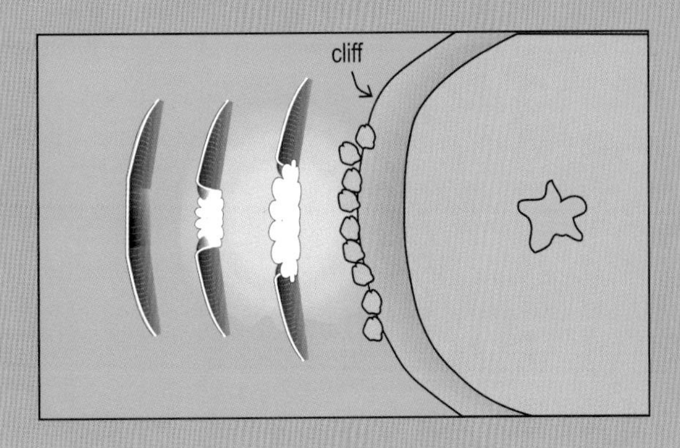

The formation of a *fajã* reef. (1) Rocks fall from the cliff top into the water below. (2) A platform is gradually formed upon which the waves are able to break.

Similarly to what happens with volcanic reefs, the natural processes that form *fajãs* can create excellent surfing waves. All that is required is the correct prevailing swell height and direction, and some world-class waves can be produced on *fajã* reefs. *Fajãs* are ideal for big waves. At some spots, the scale of the rock platform is such that ten-metre waves would theoretically not close out. Another factor that goes hand-in-hand with this is that a lot of *fajãs* are located fairly close to the shore at the base of a huge cliff or mountain, so strong offshore winds are practically a non-issue. With big waves, the last thing you want is a gale-force offshore wind magnified a hundred times up the face of the wave, making take-offs blind and dangerous.

One disadvantage of these reefs is that many of them only work well if the waves are above a certain height. If they happen to be in geographical areas where the prevailing

A fringing coral reef off a tropical island.

wave height rarely gets above that threshold, things might be frustrating. Some spot might have the potential to be world-class, but it might break only on the very biggest day of a swell. This can be annoying for those who prefer the surf to be consistent but mediocre rather than world-class just once a year. Another factor, which may be an advantage or a hindrance depending on your point of view, is the difficult access over mountainous terrain and the time required travelling from one spot to another. Lastly, although some *fajãs* have the potential to be great big-wave breaks, getting in and out of the water when the swell is really huge can sometimes be suicidal.

The magical island of Madeira, in the north-east part of the Atlantic Ocean, exemplifies the *fajã* surfing reef probably better than anywhere else in the world. Madeira is a volcanic island created about 23 million years ago by a large hotspot beneath the ocean. The island is literally a large rock sticking out of the ocean, and consists of nothing but huge, vertical cliffs, mountains and breathtaking scenery. Until relatively recently, nobody thought there could possibly be any surfable waves on Madeira, since there could be nowhere for the waves to break at the bottom of those cliffs, sometimes rising 300 m out of the sea. We now know that Madeira contains some of the best big waves in the world, almost all breaking on *fajãs*. The village that contains Madeira's most famous wave – Jardim do Mar (see page 109) – is itself built on a kind of *fajã*.

Coral

The most photogenic, crystalline barrels in the world are, without any doubt, those that break on coral reefs. The way the waves refract around the shape of the reef, combined with the quality of the swell and wind conditions, sometimes results in the waves being perfect, as if they had been drawn in a cartoon.

So, how do coral reefs come about? To start with, corals are animals, not plants. The animal, called the polyp, lives inside a skeleton of calcium carbonate, which it is continually manufacturing. When each polyp dies, it leaves its skeleton behind. A coral reef consists of millions of dead coral skeletons, formed over time, layer upon layer. Only the very superficial layer contains live corals. The reef grows over time, but growth is offset by erosion caused by the waves, currents and other sea creatures. As a result, typical growth rates of coral reefs are just a few millimetres per year. The polyps have a certain interdependence with a small algae called zooxanthellae, which live in close proximity to the polyps. It is the zooxanthellae that give coral reefs their amazing colours. Notice that, if these algae die, the reef will lose its colour – a phenomenon known as coral bleaching. This has been known to happen due to high water temperatures during *El Niño* events, and is now starting to happen due to global warming.

Coral reefs come in various shapes and sizes, and may be roughly put into three categories:

- *Fringing reefs*, which are directly attached to the land in a similar way to volcanic or other rocky reefs;
- *Barrier reefs*, which are further away from the land and separated from it by a lagoon;
- *Atolls*, which simply consist of a ring of coral around a central lagoon. Atolls contain no land at all.

These are not just different categories of coral reef; they also correspond to the various stages in the evolution of the reef. This idea, whereby the original land mass in the middle is progressively sinking relative to the sea level, was first hypothesized by Charles Darwin around 1842. Starting with a fringing reef, as the island in the middle gradually sinks, the situation progresses to a barrier reef and then, finally, to an atoll, where the land in the middle has disappeared all together. Since the live coral on the top of the reef

(1) Fringing reef.

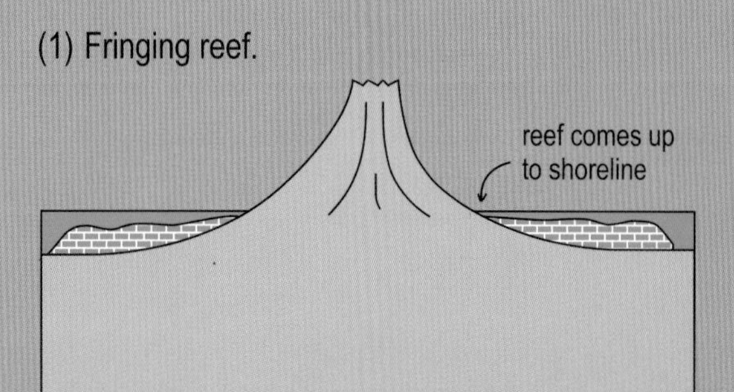

(2) Barrier reef.

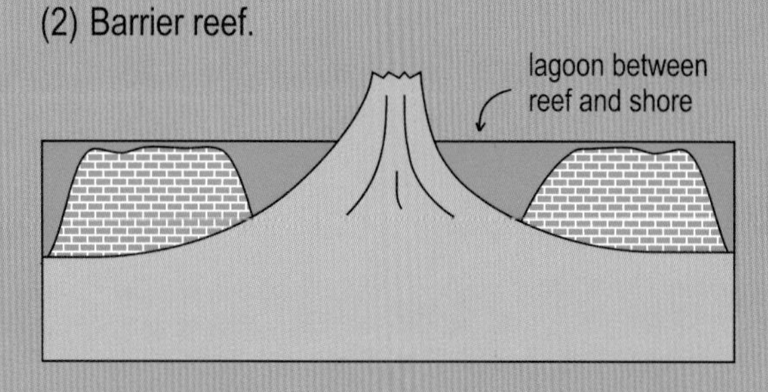

(3) Atoll.

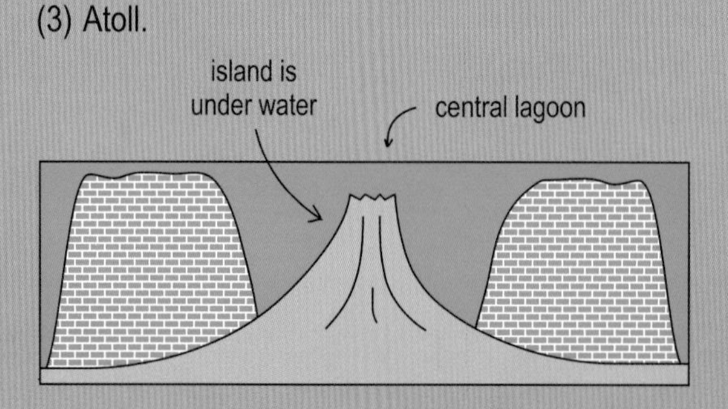

A cross-sectional slice through three types of coral reef, showing the evolution of the reef as the sea level rises relative to the volcanic island. The reef changes from a fringing reef (1) to a barrier reef (2) to an atoll (3).

can only exist in shallow water, the top of the reef must remain the same distance from the surface. Therefore, the reef can only get thicker from the bottom down, as illustrated in the diagram.

Coral reefs are found off mid-oceanic volcanic islands, typically in the Pacific, Caribbean Sea and Indian Ocean, or they can exist off continents, with the continental shelf acting as the substrate. The Great Barrier Reef of Australia is the most well known example of the latter type of reef. The most important environmental factor restricting the geographical extent of coral is water temperature: coral can only survive between about 18° and 34°C. This is the main reason why coral reefs are only found between the tropics of Cancer and Capricorn.

The natural topography of coral reefs, and the way they are constructed, makes them ideal for surfing, being relatively smooth and having the right slope for the waves to peel perfectly. But the reason why coral-reef waves tend to be perfect is not just the shape of the reef itself, although this is the main factor. It is also due to the predetermined quality of the swells that arrive at these locations. Because coral reefs are necessarily located in tropical zones, sometimes thousands of kilometres away from the storm centres, the waves almost always arrive clean and lined-up. Many of these places also have highly predictable wind regimes, with constant offshore winds for at least part of the year.

There are a few disadvantages to surfing over coral, although for most people these are far outweighed by the advantages of warm, clear water and picture-perfect barrels. The worst problem is that coral is extremely sharp – just touching the bottom means at least a nasty graze. Since you are in a tropical zone, the injury will probably become infected and, if you are not careful, you might have to stay out of the water. A nasty wipeout on the first wave could mean watching your friends get barrelled for the next two weeks. Lastly, the blazingly hot sun, malaria-carrying mosquitoes and other tropical nasties might put one or two people off.

Granite

Apart from a few exceptions, really good surfing reefs are not quite as prevalent along coasts made of granite rock as they are along other types of coasts. But it is still interesting to find out why this is so, and to look at a few general characteristics of coastlines where this ancient rock predominates.

Granite coasts are characterized by fairly low cliffs and white-sand beaches. In Europe, the prime examples of granite coasts are the peninsulas of West Cornwall, Brittany and Galicia. The granite topography adds to the special nature of these areas, with their Celtic culture, harsh beauty and rugged people. The western tip of each peninsula even carries the same name in each local language: *Land's End*, *Finisterre* and *Fisterra*.

Granite tends to come in very large, clumpy, spheroid shapes, which can often be seen sticking out of the sea, the waves crashing over them. The rock itself is extremely hard, and has a rough texture and speckled appearance. Granite is incredibly old; in some places the magma from which the rock was formed first appeared on the surface over 500 million years ago.

One of the most important factors for the quality of the surf breaking on any reef is its variation in level over a given horizontal distance: in other words, the lumpiness or unevenness of the reef. For the reef to be properly surfable, its lumpiness or roughness scale should be a lot smaller than the waves themselves. Volcanic and coral reefs, although they contain sharp edges are, in general, extremely flat on the surface compared with the waves that break on them. *Fajãs* and sedimentary-folded reefs, however, might have sudden variations in level of a metre or more, which might make getting in and out of the water difficult. More importantly, on some of these reefs, waves under about 1 m might not break in deep enough water to clear the reef, which would make the rocks actually stick out of the waves. This makes surfing uncomfortable and dangerous. Granite reefs tend to suffer from this problem quite a lot. Also the large, isolated lumps of rock often behave more like small islands than reefs, with the waves crashing into them rather than breaking over the top of them. But if the reef happens to be more of a flat, 'slab' shape, it might throw up some of the most exciting and radical types of waves around. These are normally short and extremely hollow, usually exploding dry on to the reef and then backing off into deeper water.

Wave shape and reef shape

To summarize, this chapter has categorized a few different kinds of reefs in terms of their geological formation. The surfing experience on each type of reef is different according to (a) the material the reef is made of; (b) the shape of the reef, and (c) its geographical location. The form of the breaking waves themselves is dependent on the shape of the reef, which, in turn, depends upon the underlying geology.

It is also possible to group surf spots in terms of the shape of the waves, and this has already been done in many guidebooks. The shape of the waves at some spots, however, makes them unique, and reflects a unique set of geological circumstances that produced the spot in the first place. The fact that the waves of Teahupo'o, Mavericks, Pipeline and many others are instantly recognizable puts them in categories of their own.

The other really important thing that affects the way waves break is the characteristics of the incoming swell. Its size, direction and quality – never exactly the same from one day to the next – all contribute to the overall surfing experience at a particular spot. Couple this with the vast range of possible morphological configurations, and you can see why no two waves that have broken anywhere on the planet have ever been the same.

3 Rivermouths

Some of the longest and most perfect waves break upon sandbars that form at the mouths of estuaries. Perhaps, since they break over a sand bottom, these waves ought to be referred to as beachbreaks. However, they really are quite different from normal beachbreaks, and the combination of circumstances required for the formation of good rivermouth waves is not the same as for a normal beachbreak.

Throughout this chapter I'll keep referring to Mundaka. Mundaka is, perhaps, one of the finest examples of a rivermouth wave in the world. When working properly, it can hold a 3-m swell with 400-m-long rides and open barrels. If you're lucky you can get a stand-up barrel from the beginning of the wave to the end. However, between about 2003 and 2006 the wave at Mundaka almost disappeared, due to a set of circumstances triggered by human intervention. Using the case of Mundaka, I shall try to illustrate how complex and fragile estuarine systems are, particularly those containing world-class surfing waves.

The estuarine sandbar 'machine'

Many different aspects of estuaries are studied by scientists, including the way the water flow behaves according to wave and tidal motions; the balance between fresh and salt water; how different types of sediments are found in different parts of the estuary; the long- and short-term behaviour of the flora and fauna and its interaction with the physics of the system, and, not least, the sandbar that inevitably forms at the mouth of the estuary.

Most estuaries contain a sandbar, or a series of them, at the estuary's mouth. Large boat owners tend to see them as unnecessary impediments to navigation, sent from hell just to make their lives more difficult. To surfers, they are a wonder of Nature, sent from heaven specifically to produce long and perfect barrels. To scientists, they are a highly dynamic aspect of estuarine systems that urgently needs to be understood, not least because the effects of any intervention by large boat owners might be felt most severely by surfers.

Over long time-scales, estuarine sandbars should not change, provided that the whole system remains 'healthy'. The average position of the bar and its average size and shape should remain fairly constant over time-scales spanning a year or more. Changes do occur, however, over shorter, seasonal time-scales. During periods of calm or relatively small waves, the bar is built up by a combination of gentle wave action bringing sediment in from the sea, and the flow of the river together with the outgoing tide, bringing sediment down from the land. Then, during episodic storm events or periods of relatively large waves, the more aggressive action of the waves tends to erode the bar away, spreading the sediment out over a larger area.

So, how exactly does the bar build itself up during periods of small waves? Well, the first mechanism, the way in which sediments get deposited on to the bar from the sea, is similar to the way in which sandbars are formed on normal beaches. Just offshore of the breakpoint, there is a slight, onshore-directed net movement of water, so any sediment scooped off the bottom outside of the breakpoint is carried onshore. This mechanism takes a relatively minor role and is only noticeable during long periods of persistently small waves. The second mechanism – far more significant for building up the bar – is from the flow of the river itself, augmented by the strong outgoing (ebb) tidal flow. During the ebb tide, the two flows are superimposed upon each other, resulting in a strong seaward-flowing current, which has the capacity to scoop up large amounts of sediment from the bed. This sediment then flows down the river and is deposited on the bar.

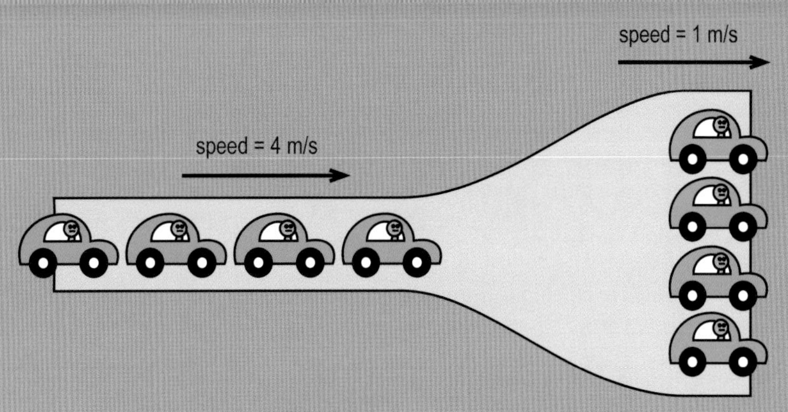

The conservation of mass in a widening road. The volumetric flow rate is 4 cars per second (4 cars must pass a given point every second). If a car is 1 m long, then it follows that, to maintain the flow rate, the cars must travel at 4 metres per second (m/s) to get four of them through the narrow part in a second, and at 1 m/s to get four of them through the wide part in a second.

To understand exactly how the sediment gets deposited on the bar, and why it doesn't just continue on out to sea, we need to introduce two very basic physical concepts: the *conservation of mass* and the *threshold of sediment suspension*.

The idea of conservation of mass is very simple. Imagine water flowing down a hosepipe, the water being supplied at a constant rate by a tap on the wall. The number of cubic centimetres of water coming out of the end of that pipe every second (the *volumetric flow rate*) *must* match the number of cubic centimetres entering it from the tap, otherwise something weird would happen (water would have to mysteriously appear or disappear in the pipe). Now, if you squeeze the end of that pipe, the water shoots out faster. Why? Because the volumetric flow rate has to be maintained; all those cubic centimetres of water must travel that much faster to get out through a smaller hole in the same time. The same applies if you make the opening bigger – the volume of water has a wider area to flow through, so it can spread itself out more and can afford to go more slowly. If you're still not sure about this, think of a stream of traffic. To maintain the 'volumetric flow rate' of the traffic, the cars must go faster where the road is narrower, and/or slower where the road is wider. As an example, let's say the 'volumetric flow rate' is four cars per second (four cars must pass a given point every second, as in the diagram). The width of the road suddenly changes from one car's width to four cars' width. To keep the flow going at a constant four cars per second, the cars must travel four times as fast in the narrow part as in the wide part. That, basically, is the conservation of mass. You can see it in action everywhere – not just in hosepipes and on motorways, but in rip currents, wind blowing through buildings in a city, egg timers and, of course, in estuaries.

The other concept is just as simple. Imagine water flowing along in a stream or river where the bed is made up of sediment. The water 'rubbing' on the bed produces turbulence which lifts up some of the sediment and suspends it in the water. The sediment, of course, immediately tries to fall back down under the force of gravity. If the turbulence is strong enough, it will keep the sediment in suspension; or, at least, keep the amount of suspended sediment constant by scooping up more grains from the bed as other ones fall down. For the turbulence to be strong enough to do this, the velocity of the water has to be above a certain threshold. That is the threshold of sediment suspension. If the water velocity goes below this threshold, the force of gravity overbalances the turbulence and the grains start to fall out.

Now, we need to combine the two basic principles of conservation of mass and threshold of suspension in an estuary. The water flowing fast over the bed, particularly on the outgoing tide, suspends sediment and keeps it suspended in the river. The river continues picking up sediment as it flows out towards the sea. The water is flowing fast enough so that the sediment continues to be carried in the water without falling out. At the mouth of the estuary, the width of the river increases dramatically. So, to conserve the volumetric flow rate, the water, laden with sediment, must decrease its velocity. As soon as the water slows down to below the sediment suspension threshold, the sediment falls out. It is here that the sediment accumulates on the bed to form a bar, as you can see in the diagram.

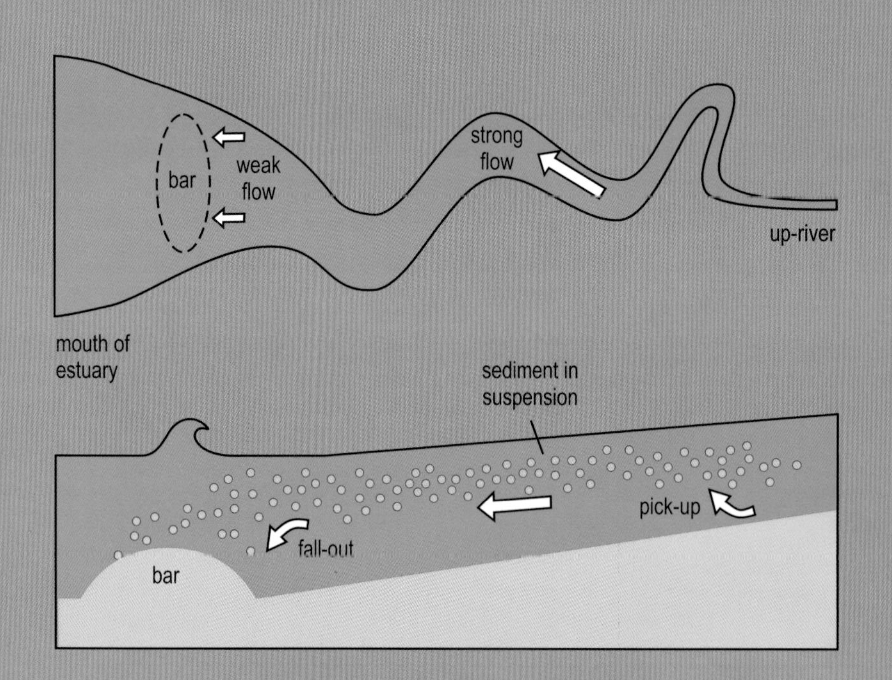

How an estuarine sandbar is built up in small-wave conditions. The seaward flow due to the river and ebb tide is strong enough upstream to scoop up sediment and keep it in suspension. Once this flow reaches the mouth, the extra width of the estuary makes it slow down to below a critical threshold, whereby the sediment can no longer be kept in suspension. At this point the sediment falls out, and the bar is formed.

One of several excellent Spanish rivermouth setups.

How can an estuary produce a perfect wave?

There are thousands of estuaries in the world. Not all of them have a wave like Mundaka. In fact, only a very small proportion of them have any kind of surfable wave at all. This is because the existence of such a wave depends upon a number of factors, all of which must be exactly right. Here are a few examples:

- The scale of the river and the estuary must be just right compared with the scale of the waves. Many estuaries have a bar that only produces perfect 2-cm waves, while others have a bar that would produce perfect waves if only it received regular 60-m swells. Some estuaries might be set up perfectly for waves between one and three metres, but be situated in a fjord where it is always flat.
- The shape of the bar must be just right. This dictates the shape of the wave itself – whether it ends up being the 400-m barrel that everybody wants, or a slow wave that sections or backs off. The shape of the bar itself depends on the combination of other factors, such as the type and size of the sediment, and the characteristics of the riverflow.
- The prevailing direction and quality of the incoming swells must combine perfectly with the orientation of the bar. To peel properly down the length of the bar, the waves must come in at an oblique angle; if they come in 'square-on' they will just close out. This might depend upon not just the orientation of the coast where the estuary is situated, but also on whether the waves have previously been interfered with – for example, refracted around a nearby headland or island.
- The prevailing wind conditions must be just right. If the prevailing wind is onshore, then it doesn't matter how perfect the local geology or swell quality is: the waves will be choppy and uncomfortable to ride.

There are probably many more factors, but the general point I want to make is that only a small percentage of the estuaries in the world comply with any one of these factors, let alone all of them. Maybe only 10 per cent of the world's estuaries have a bar that is the right scale to produce the waves we want. How many of these 10 per cent also have a bar that is just the right shape to produce a good wave? Not many – maybe 2 per cent (2 per cent of 10 per cent – we're already down to 0.2 per cent). Then, how many of these also have good prevailing wind conditions and regular, long-lined swells of the right size and direction? Not many. So you can see that the number we end up with is going to be pretty small.

Also, the system has to be stable and consistent. A perfect wave might appear one year in some estuary, but that might have been a freak combination of excess riverflow due to a lot of snow on the mountains, a run of westerly swells and unusual southerly winds, or some other anomalous set of circumstances. For a perfect wave to appear on a regular basis is much more difficult: it requires all those factors to be right, all or at least most of the time.

Resilience, feedback and chaos

If the process I described above of sediment pick-up, suspension and fall-out continues, the bar will just keep on growing, especially during periods of calm or small waves. Of course, this doesn't happen. Instead, every now and again, there is a large storm or swell, which tends to erode the sediment off the bar and distort its shape. The big waves break hard on the bar and displace the sediment over a wider area, carrying it back out to sea or along the coast. This creates a balance between two opposing forces: the outgoing flows of the river and the ebb tide which build up the bar, and the action of large or stormy waves which erode it away again.

In an estuary containing a good surfing wave, there might be certain times of year when the bar is at its optimum, and other times when it just isn't quite right. This depends upon the balance between the *accretionary mechanisms* (riverflow plus ebb-tidal current), and the *erosionary mechanisms* (the action of large swells or stormy waves). Typically, the bar might be in good shape just after a long period of small swells or calm conditions. The sediment has gradually been accumulating into a nice smooth 'hump', ready for the first swells of the season to break perfectly. However, every time a swell hits the bar, particularly if it is a big one, the bar tends to be worn away, destroying that nice hump and making the wave less perfect. If the big swells continue, the bar, and the waves that break on it, will end up in bad shape. As soon as the storms abate, however, the bar will begin to recover its hump, and, after a while, be in perfect shape once again ready for the next swells.

So the bar is at its best after long periods of calm or very small waves, and becomes worse the more large waves break on it. It has a kind of intrinsic self-limitation. In other words, there is a certain restriction on the number of good waves we can extract from it. The self-limiting nature of an estuarine bar system is a good example of a *negative-feedback loop*. Negative feedback is not just found in dynamical systems driven by the laws of chaos, but can be seen regularly in everyday life. Take your own stomach, for example: the more you eat, the fuller you get, the less hungry you become. The sensation of fullness is transmitted from your stomach to your brain, telling it to make you feel less hungry and, therefore, to stop eating. If it wasn't for that negative feedback loop, you'd eat until you exploded.

Dani Garcia, deep inside a rivermouth tube near Santander, Spain.

In the case of an estuary, the constant play-off between the riverflow and the wave action prevents the system from being thrown permanently out of balance. The amount of negative feedback is automatically adjusted to keep things from straying too far. For example, after a period of strong riverflow and/or little wave action, the bar will have built up to such an extent that the water will be particularly shallow. Any small swells that didn't break before will tend to break now, and any bigger ones will be strongly focused on to the bar and break particularly heavily. The waves will 'bite' into the bar more, and so are likely to erode it away more quickly. However, as soon as the bar has actually been eroded by a few days of big waves, the water at the breakpoint will be deeper again. This extra depth of water means that the waves will no longer have the same eroding effect. Moreover, the bar, now depleted of its sediment, will be just begging for more sediment to flow down from the river. Negative feedback is constantly steering the system back on a course towards equilibrium.

Importantly, this cyclic behaviour should remain stable in the long term. Over an extended period – say an entire year – there should be no overall change in the average size and shape of the bar. If the wave and riverflow characteristics are highly seasonal, then at any given time of year, give or take a month or so, the bar should look more or less the same as it did last year. For some systems, this averaging might apply over longer or shorter periods.

So, in the long term, the state of the bar is *resilient* to any permanent changes. Thanks to negative feedback, it tends to spring back automatically to that stable state, even if abused with excessive riverflow or wave action. If that state is one that produces good waves, then we are in luck. We can even abuse the system ourselves, to a certain extent, perhaps by digging out sediment in one place and dumping it in another. Usually, the system can cope, eventually reverting to its state of equilibrium. We can borrow a term from the jargon of chaos and call this state of equilibrium an *attractor*.

If any of the overall characteristics of the system change – for example, the normal range of wave heights and riverflow rates; the angle of wave approach, or the physical dimensions and shape of the estuary – then the system might look for a different attractor state. In other words, the bar will change permanently. This kind of thing normally happens over geological time-scales, but it can be grossly accelerated with human activities, such as the construction of a dam that permanently cuts off the sediment supply, or a harbour or pier that blocks off the waves or changes their direction of approach.

However, the system can also flip into a different state if it is temporarily over-abused, or pushed beyond some threshold. Rare climatic anomalies, such as extreme droughts, heavy rains, or uncharacteristically huge swells from unusual directions, can do this. So can over-dredging or dumping of too much sand in the estuary. The important thing to realize is that, even after we stop the abuse, and take the pressure off, the system might not want to go back to its old attractor. It has found a new one, and there it will stay. Getting it to go back again might then be impossible.

If you are confused about attractor states, then think of a light switch. A light switch has two attractor states: 'on' and 'off'. It can withstand all sorts of abuse from the environment (air-pressure changes, flies landing on the switch, major vibrations in the wall), and will still spring back to the same state. Only when we deliberately apply pressure in a certain way, does the switch reach a stage where it finds it easier to flip into the other state than to spring back to the first one. When we then take the pressure off, the switch stays there in its new state; it doesn't flip back again.

The difference between a light switch and an estuary is that a light switch has only two attractor states, whereas an estuary might have thousands of subtly different ones. It is also possible that the system be left in a kind of chaotic half-state, either randomly varying for ever and never settling down, or vacillating from one state to another like an old sparking light switch that doesn't know if it's on or off, the light bulb flickering aimlessly.

Getting an estuarine sandbar back to its original state after some freak climatic event or human interference has flipped it into another state, might not be so simple. If we try to get it back by once again exceeding its natural thresholds, it might flip into yet

Classic view from the 'Atalaya' of the world's most famous rivermouth: Mundaka.

another completely different state, or it might continue to flitter about randomly. If the wave breaking on that estuarine sandbar happens to have been so perfect that you couldn't imagine it any better, then any change will, by definition, make it worse.

Mundaka

Mundaka is a small Spanish fishing village at the mouth of the River Oka, in the Urdaibai Biosphere Reserve, declared as such by UNESCO in 1984. It is close to the historical Basque town of Gernika, immortalized by Picasso's famous painting depicting how it was bombed in 1937 under the orders of Francisco Franco.

When the first surfers turned up at Mundaka around the late 1960s and set their eyes upon those perfect lefthanders, they had no reason to think those waves wouldn't be there all the time. Or, at least, every time there was a good swell. From the mid-1980s to the early 1990s, when the North Atlantic Ocean hit an all-time high in terms of wave power, Mundaka was never better. It was relatively uncrowded, and, every single day, or so it seemed, there were waves that just barrelled from one end to the other. At the time, the local surfers thought it would go on for ever. We now know that Mundaka neither breaks perfectly every time there is a swell, nor is it constantly 6–8 ft and barrelling from one end to the other. We also now know that Mundaka is a very special wave. Not just because of its perfection, power or length, but also because of the miraculous circumstances that made it the way it is. Sure, there are lefts just as long and hollow as Mundaka (Grajagan, Tavarua and many others), but they all break on immovable rock or coral platforms. Mundaka is the only wave of its class to break on a rivermouth sandbar.

So what makes Mundaka so special? Some of the physical factors that happen to be just right to make Mundaka such a good wave, perhaps even unique, include the following:

- The average height, period and quality of the swells received along the part of the coast where Mundaka is situated are pretty good (with the right set-up they can happily produce 8–10-ft barrels).
- The average riverflow and ebb-tidal current speeds are just right – they bring the right amount of sediment down the river at the right times of the year; the raw swells first have to wrap around a headland called Cabo Matxitxako, about 4 km before they get to the break – the filtering action of the headland means that the waves reaching Mundaka take the form of long, ruler-edged lines rather than shifting peaks.
- If the wind is from the west-south-west, south-west or south, the action of the river valley funnels it round to the south, which is offshore.
- The orientation of the outer edge of the sandbar with respect to the orientation of the incoming swells is at the perfect angle so that the wave is not too fast and not too slow.
- The outer edge of the bar is straight enough for the wave to go on breaking at the right speed along its entire length.
- The depth graduation of the outer edge of the bar is the perfect angle, so that the wave is a round, open barrel from beginning to end.

Mundaka goes wrong

In the early days, the overriding concern among local surfers was how they themselves could make the best of the wave – how they could improve board design and riding techniques to get in and out of those freight-train barrels as easily as possible. They had no idea that, eventually, their principal concern would turn from dominating the wave to protecting it.

In recent years, Mundaka seems to have been gradually losing some of its magic. There are constant crowds in the water – sometimes up to 200 – bringing with them the inevitable conflicts and stress. The yearly international contest has become a million-dollar affair, with the wave predictably being viewed by some as nothing more than a source of income. Not only that, but, recently, due to a large dredging operation by a local shipbuilding company, and a subsequent chain of physical processes that nobody was able to predict, Mundaka came close to death. The quality of the wave was reduced, for a time at least, from a ten-out-of-ten, world-class to a two-out-of-ten, barely surfable.

Even taking into account seasonal variations and other perturbations due to the regular human interference that has taken place over the last half century, Mundaka never quite looked the way it did between about 2003 and 2006. At the normal take-off spot, during low-tide springs, the water depth, which should normally be about 0.5 m, was about 6 m. The main riverflow was now ending up in the middle of the estuary instead of to the western side of it, meaning that the bar (formed at the head of the main riverflow) had shifted towards the middle of the estuary. The new bar was orientated square-on to the incoming waves, making them close out, back off and close out again. Mundaka was reduced from a

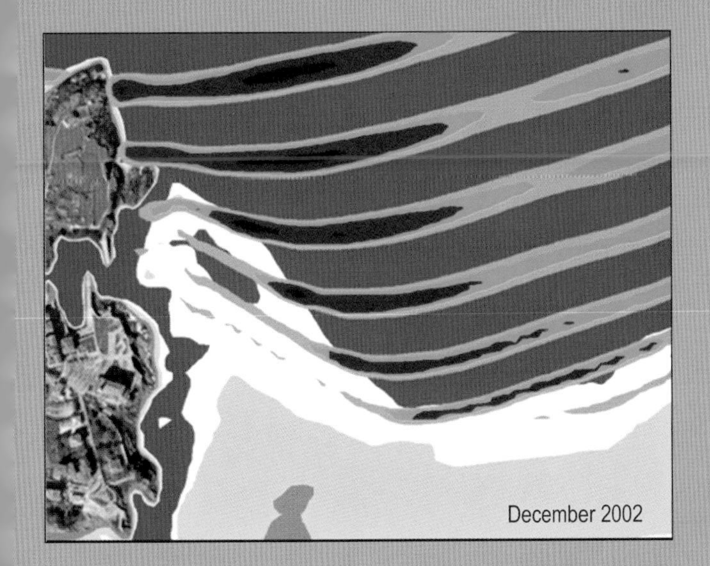

Simulations of 1-m waves breaking at Mundaka. The shape of the sandbar, depicted in white, is real and was measured carefully using GPS equipment in December 2002 (top panel) and May 2005 (bottom panel). The waves, in blue, were 'generated' using a computer model, and 'propagated' on to the measured bathymetry. You can see how well the waves peel down the edge of the sandbar in December 2002, and how bad it was in May 2005.

world-class pointbreak to a poor-quality beachbreak, as illustrated in the diagrams.

After this situation continued for a couple of seasons, local surfers started to realize that it might not be just part of the natural behaviour of the bar, and started getting worried that it might never recover. People began to look for an ultimate cause for the possible permanent degradation of one of the world's finest waves. The climatic patterns over the previous few years had been different from those of, say, 15 years before, with much less storminess in the North Atlantic and fewer big swells reaching Mundaka. Winter 2004–05 was practically devoid of big surf, apart from one huge storm with nearby wavebuoys registering over 9 m. That unusual pattern may have contributed to the detriment of the bar, or it may have been a number of other, perhaps totally unknown, factors. However, the event most likely to have been the original catalyst was the shifting of some 243,000 cubic metres of sand, performed by a local shipbuilding company, during the period March to June 2003. The sand was dredged out from the usual channel to facilitate the removal of a particularly large ship. Dredging the channel to float ships out had been done many times during the previous 40 years, with very little noticeable effect on the sandbar. This time, though, far more sand was removed in one go than ever before.

The sand that was removed from the channel was deposited on the other side of the estuary and up-river to 'regenerate' a sand dune. The perpetrators thought they could kill two birds with one stone. Most of that sand was eroded away immediately, and ended up diverting the course of the river, putting the main outgoing flow to one side of the original sandbar. The sandbar in its original position was no longer being continually fed with sediment, and therefore was no longer being maintained in position.

Miraculously, some time between October and December 2006, the bar did actually recover. In the end, it never reached that new state of equilibrium, and was flipped back to its original one. But that doesn't mean all that fuss was for nothing, and that we can carry on abusing the system. The effects of the dredging were still making the situation worse more than two years after it was done. It seems that the system was triggered by that dredging, and sent off on a chaotic path where it dithered around for about three years before something managed to flip it back to its original state.

So how close did it get to not flipping back? Imagine if, one day, somebody dredged 243,001 instead of 243,000 cubic metres from the estuary. That might just be enough to make it never return, continuing for ever in chaotic limbo, fibrillating meaninglessly from one half-state to another, or reaching some new attractor state with a mid-estuary bar producing nothing but useless close-outs. I hope we never find out. And although the wave seems to have recovered, I hope people will not forget this important part of the story of Mundaka. Mundaka almost went down in history as the most tragic case of a perfect surfing wave, unique in the world, destroyed by greed and short-sightedness. Hopefully, it will now be known as one of

For a time it was thought that this view would never be enjoyed again at Mundaka.

the world's finest surfing waves that came *so close* to being destroyed by greed and short-sightedness that those responsible will think a little more carefully before interfering so blatantly with something none of us understands very well.

Climate and Big Waves

This section is mostly about the climatology of the waves – how oceanic storminess fluctuates over seasons, years and decades, and how wave height and quality vary throughout the oceans of the world. This is useful information if we want to learn what factors influence the ups and downs of wave heights at one particular location over short and long time-scales, and also if we want to find out when and where to look for good waves. If you are interested in looking for big surf, then some knowledge of wave climatology is even more useful, if not essential. So, this section is deliberately biased towards big waves.

First, we take a look at climatic cycles and the ups and downs of oceanic storminess. By recognizing certain cyclic patterns in the atmosphere and ocean, we can begin to understand why good swells, even good winters, tend to come in 'sets', just like the waves themselves. There are a whole host of these climatic cycles, operating in the North Atlantic, the North Pacific, the South Pacific, and the Southern Oceans, each behaving in its own subtly different way. Here, we concentrate on the most well-known ones, and the ones most obviously affecting the waves we ride.

Then we switch focus to how, when and where to look for the biggest surfable waves. We look around the world's oceans to find the largest wind-generated waves inside the storms themselves, and then find out how far away from those storm centres the swells have to travel before becoming clean enough to ride. We investigate crucial factors affecting the surfability of big waves near the storm centre, and other factors that work to re-boost their size after propagating great distances.

Lastly, we have an ironic look at 'where it all might end'. The last chapter in this section is about the absurdity of some recently proposed projects to artificially modify the climate. We apply those ideas to big-wave riding by telling the story of a future scenario in which huge waves are generated artificially in the Pacific Ocean for the most spectacular big wave contest ever.

4 Climatic cycles, storminess and surf

Cyclic behaviour is everywhere you look, especially when it comes to the ocean and atmosphere. It is evident in the waves themselves, whose height oscillates with each set, swell and season; the wind, whose strength fluctuates with every gust, storm and season; the tides, whose range varies with springs and neaps, and from year to year; and then much larger-scale cycles over decades, centuries and millennia, such as ice ages and the evolution of the planet itself.

Climatologists are always looking for clues as to how to better understand the long-term weather patterns of this planet, and the identification of cyclic behaviour in the climate is a good step. The North Atlantic Oscillation, and oscillations in the North and South Pacific Oceans linked to the *El Niño* Southern Oscillation cycle, were recognized as long ago as 1924, by Sir Gilbert Walker. However, it is only recently that vast increases in data and computing power have enabled scientists to study these cycles in much greater detail. And the prospect of important climatic changes due to global warming has provided added motivation to investigate these cycles.

There are a confusing number of climatic cycles, all related to each other, and some a lot more dominant than others. Although scientists have had a grip on the *El Niño* Southern Oscillation and the North Atlantic Oscillation for some years, the other cycles are much less well understood. What is certain, however, is that, to some extent, the ocean and atmosphere everywhere on the planet behave in a periodic manner, but in different ways according to the particular area of the planet. This chapter gives a basic description of the particular cycles that are known to have a direct relation to the storminess of the oceans, the waves we ride, and the moulding of the shape of the coast.

The North Atlantic Oscillation

If you are somewhere on the west coast of Europe, and you are reading this because it is winter and there is no surf, chances are the North Atlantic Ocean contains a blocking anticyclone. The blocking anticyclone is a large area of high pressure that sometimes takes residence in the middle of the North Atlantic, literally blocking any swell-forming low pressures, and abolishing any prospects of decent surf on the west coasts of Europe. The blocking high is a mysterious phenomenon that probably goes unnoticed by 90 per cent of the population; however, if you are a surfer living in Ireland, Wales, Cornwall, France, Spain or Portugal, then the blocking high is a vital determining factor for the consistency and size of the surf. Its presence might mean long spells of weak or non-existent surf, and cold northerly winds; and its absence might mean a string of big, powerful swells, and light, warm, southerly winds.

The blocking anticyclone is the major feature of one half of a two-phase climatological see-saw called the North Atlantic Oscillation (NAO). When the anticyclone is present (the 'blocking' phase), any low pressures are sent either far northwards towards Greenland or north of Iceland, or southwards towards the Azores or the Canary Islands. In either case, the lows do not get much of a chance to deepen, or to generate decent swells. In contrast, when the blocking anticyclone is missing (the 'fluid', or 'mobile' phase), low pressures are easily allowed to form, deepen and track quickly from west to east across the North Atlantic, sending pulses of swell westwards and southwards.

The length of time that each phase of the NAO lasts can vary from a couple of days to several months, but it is typically around one to two weeks. You might get a run of big swells or particularly stormy conditions lasting, say, ten days; and then, without warning, the situation suddenly changes, and the blocking anticyclone once again establishes itself. Each one of these situations is, to a certain extent, self-perpetuating. For example, once that blocking anticyclone appears, it will quickly become a very stable feature. Factors that work to destroy it are constantly amassing; but, until they become strong enough to tip the balance, nothing seems to happen. Then, one day, the system can no longer maintain itself in that state, and it collapses and flips into the other state.

As far as the general weather in Europe is concerned, when the Atlantic is in its 'fluid' phase and the blocking anticyclone is absent, the European weather tends to be milder and wetter, with the westerlies bringing moist air from the ocean. In the 'blocking' phase, with the anticyclone present, the weather becomes colder and dryer, often with strong north-easterly winds bringing cold air from Siberia.

The NAO also has a kind of 'see-saw' effect on the waves. If you live on the east coast of the UK, or any other North Sea surfing area, or in the Mediterranean, a 'blocking' pattern is sometimes advantageous. A low pressure over Scandinavia, combined with the Atlantic anticyclone, means a long passage of northerly gales feeding into the top of the North Sea, generating big northerly swells. In the Mediterranean, some lows could end up stalling and re-deepening after passing to the south of the blocking high. Havoc would be wreaked in many tourist resorts; but at the same time, a healthy supply of waves would be delivered to the often surf-starved population.

To quantify, in a simple way, where the North Atlantic is at any given time within its pendulum-like existence, scientists use a single number called the NAO index. This is based on the difference in atmospheric pressure between a spot in the north of the North Atlantic (typically Iceland) and another in the south (typically the Azores or Gibraltar). If the pressure is abnormally low in the north and/or abnormally high in the south, that suggests the 'fluid' phase, with a strong westerly air stream over the ocean, lots of low pressures and lots of surf in Western Europe. If the pressure is abnormally high in the north, and/or abnormally low in the south, there is probably a blocking anticyclone sitting there and, among other things, little in the way of surf for western Europe.

The variation of the NAO has a lot to do with the flow of air at high altitudes. The mid-latitude jet stream – the atmospheric 'super-highway' that flows from west to east around the planet at altitudes of between 5,000 and 10,000 m – is highly influential for the movement and development of weather systems on the surface. The orientation of the jet is instrumental in dictating the way surface low pressure systems form and move; and it is therefore very important for the surf. Generally, the path taken by a surface low follows the track of the jet stream. Also, the amount of energy pumped into the low depends upon the strength of the jet and its orientation. The deepest lows tend to form in places where the jet stream is strongest, and where the flow is straight and pointing slightly towards the north-east: for example, in the North Atlantic, between, say, the Eastern Seaboard of the USA and Northern Scotland.

Whether the upper air flow is relatively straight, or has large meanders in it, is a key factor. If the jet is flowing straight, smooth and fast across the Atlantic, this will be favourable for the 'fluid' phase of the NAO, with the rapid formation and propagation of surface lows. For a blocking anticyclone to form, the upper air stream over the North Atlantic tends to have an omega-shaped pattern, with relatively high pressure extending down to the surface in the middle of the omega. These transitory wobbles in the upper air flow are referred to as *planetary waves* or *Rossby waves*, after the famous Swedish meteorologist Carl Gustaf Rossby. Their alternate appearance

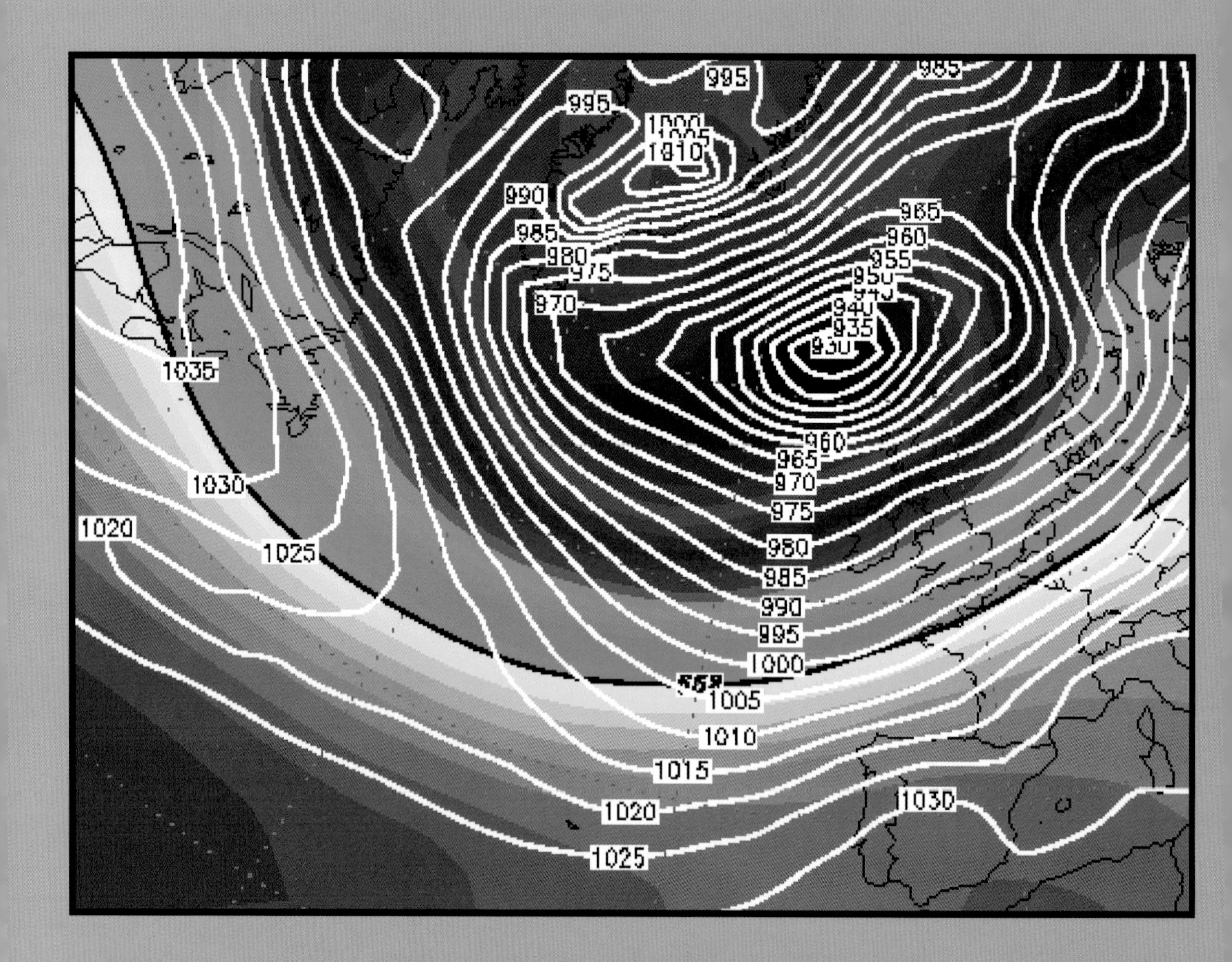

The Braer Storm, a few hours after its central pressure was recorded at 915 mb. In the picture, the low has 'filled' to 930 mb. This chart represents the fluid phase of the North Atlantic Oscillation, with the NAO index (the pressure over the Azores minus the pressure over Iceland) running at around 80 mb. The upper air flow, shown by the thick black line, has no meanders in it over the ocean.

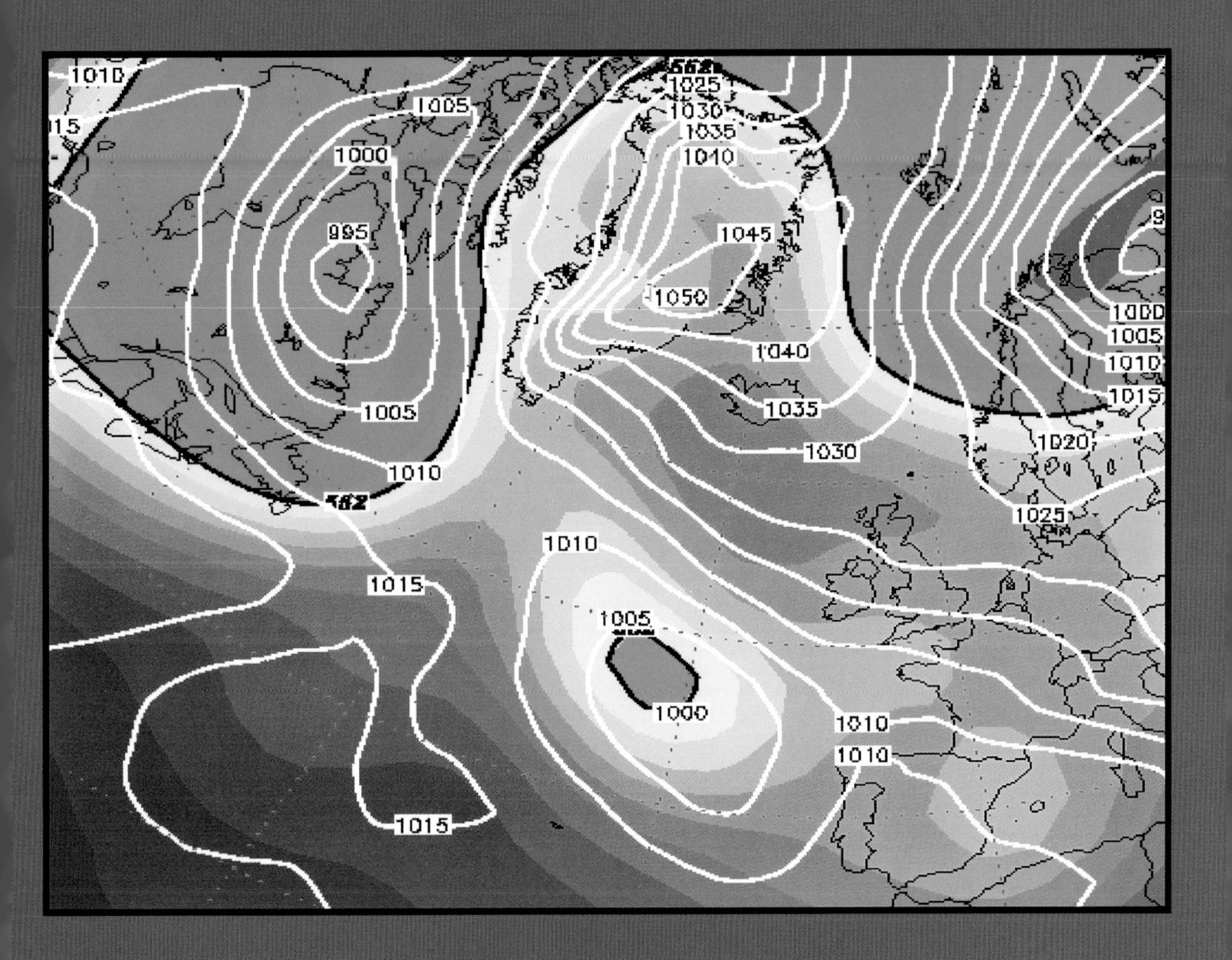

This chart represents the blocking phase of the North Atlantic Oscillation, with the pressure over the Azores actually lower than that over Iceland (an NAO index of minus 25 mb). The upper air flow, shown by the thick black line, has a huge meander in it.

and disappearance is closely related to the phases of the NAO. They are reminiscent of meanders in a giant river; as one of these meanders grows and grows, eventually a point is reached when the river takes a short cut, suddenly straightening the main flow and jettisoning the meander as an isolated vortex, doomed to weaken and die. At this point the whole cycle starts again, with a small perturbation becoming amplified into another large meander, and so on.

The NAO has a continuum of different scales of variation, from days to years or even decades. But within these embedded cycles are two fluctuation periods more important to us than the others. The first is the 'blocking' to 'fluid' and back to 'blocking' pattern that might last from a few days to a couple of months. This has a direct effect on the surf, with the North Atlantic either regularly turning out swell-producing depressions, or choked-up with a vast anticyclone. The other important time-scale of variation is much longer: this is associated with whole runs of winters where either one phase or the other tends to predominate. In any given winter, the system flips from one phase to the other several times. Over an entire winter, the total, cumulative time in one state might be more than the total cumulative time in the other state, which is what determines the overall storminess of that winter. Furthermore, it appears that stormy winters tend to come clustered together, which suggests that relative storminess and relative calmness alternate over scales of many years and decades.

One very useful thing we can do with the NAO index is to directly relate it to the surf. The NAO index can tell us whether we are currently in a 'blocking' or a 'fluid' phase, and we already know that there is more chance of big surf in the North Atlantic if we are in a 'fluid' phase. Therefore, the NAO index should tell us, in a simple way, whether the waves are likely to be big or small: a large, positive NAO index means big waves, and a small or negative NAO index means small waves.

Taken over long time-scales, the NAO index, with its ups and downs, can be used as a 'proxy' for wave heights. This might enable us to see how wave heights in the North Atlantic varied in the past, and, perhaps, give us a clue as to how they might vary in the future. First, however, we should see exactly how well the NAO index 'performs' as a predictor of North Atlantic wave heights. In scientific research, if values of one parameter are to be used to infer values of another, then the two should first be 'calibrated' against each other using as much real data as possible. David Woolf at the Southampton Oceanography Centre has already done this. Over a relatively short calibration period, he compared wave-height data with NAO-index data, to see how well correlated they were. Wave-height data were obtained from satellite observations, over the period

A classic low-pressure system centred just south-west of Iceland – perfect for producing surf in Western Europe.

A severe storm at Porthleven, south Cornwall, England, December 1989. Numerous such storms hit the UK during a peak in NAO-index values in the late 1980s and early 1990s.

1991 to 2000. These values were then tested against NAO-index values using atmospheric pressure data from Iceland and Gibraltar for the same period. Woolf concluded that long-term trends in North-Atlantic wave heights can, indeed, be mimicked by the NAO index. Also, because he had wave-height data not just for one point on the ocean but for a whole grid covering the entire North Atlantic, he was able to construct contour plots showing how well the NAO index performs as a wave-height proxy over different areas of the ocean. For example, very good correlations were found around north-west Scotland, Northern Ireland and the Bay of Biscay, but worse correlations at the Seven Stones light vessel at the western end of the English Channel.

So now we know we can look at the long-term history of North-Atlantic wave heights through the 'window' of the NAO index with reasonable confidence. This is really useful if we want to look back into the past and see what the wave heights were like, but don't actually have any real wave data. For example, NAO-index values are available going back to at least 1820, but wave-height data are not available for anywhere near that length of time. So, using that data, I plotted a time series of the NAO index from 1820 to 2004 (see diagram on page 54). The same ups and downs can therefore be assumed for the wave heights. You can see that, between around 1960 and 1990 there was a steady increase in values, followed by a steady decline between about 1990 and 2004. If you zoomed in and just looked at the section between 1960 and 1990, you might be forgiven for thinking that wave heights and storminess were experiencing a systematic increase, and might continue to intensify. However, now we have the bigger picture, we can see that this was just a particularly large upward swing of a pattern that is cyclic. We can also see that the NAO took a long dive between about 1920 and 1960, and the increase in storminess towards the end of the twentieth century was just the NAO recovering from this plummet. This long dip in values, covering almost half the length of time covered by the measurements, suggests that we still don't really have enough data. We cannot be sure whether the long dip was part of a very, very long cycle, which we would have to look back many hundreds of years to resolve, or whether it was just a one-off anomaly.

If we had enough sea-level pressure data to calculate NAO-index values going back far enough, we could extend the above analysis back into the past millennium. But we don't. One thing we *can* do though is to find yet another parameter for which we *do* have hundreds of years of data, and use that to infer NAO-index values. We can then use those inferred NAO-index values to infer the wave heights. It would be a kind of 'second-order' proxy; not as precise or accurate as a 'first-order' scheme, but of some use nevertheless. If we don't stick our neck out too far and make too many assumptions, we might be able to use this technique to learn a little more about the cyclic behaviour of North-Atlantic storminess and wave heights over really long time-scales.

The first problem is to find the right parameter. It must be related somehow to the NAO, and it must be available over time spans of at least a few hundred years. For this purpose, the two most commonly used parameters at the moment are tree rings and ice cores. For example, Mary Glueck and Charles Stockton of the Laboratory of Tree-Ring Research at the University of Arizona have done an extensive NAO 'reconstruction' using a combination of these two parameters. Using tree-ring chronologies from Morocco and Finland combined with ice cores from Greenland, they were able to reconstruct an impressive 555-year record of NAO-index values spanning from 1429 to 1983. The tree rings were used to indicate changes in rainfall, and the ice cores to indicate changes in temperature, both of

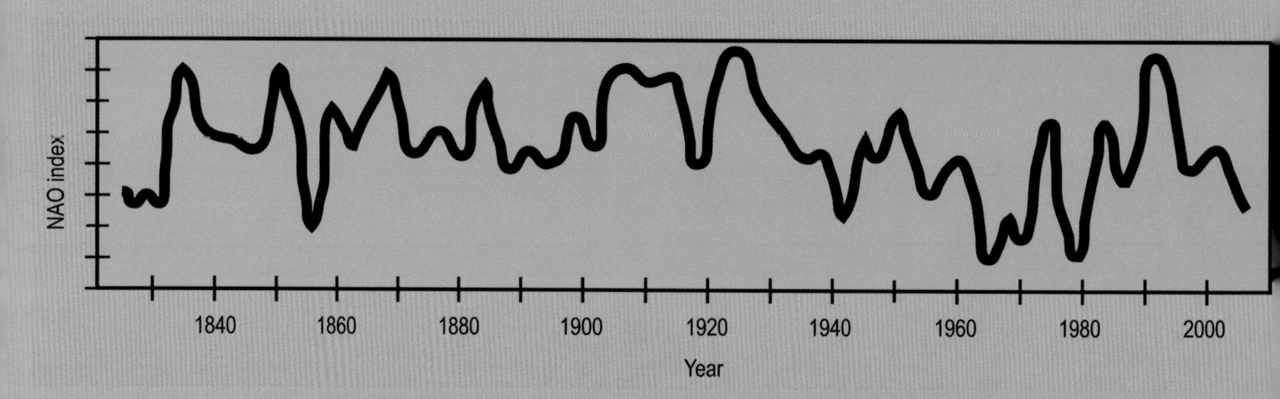

Time series of NAO index, from 1820 to 2004. The ups and downs can be related directly to wave heights in the North Atlantic. The peak around 1990 can be clearly seen.

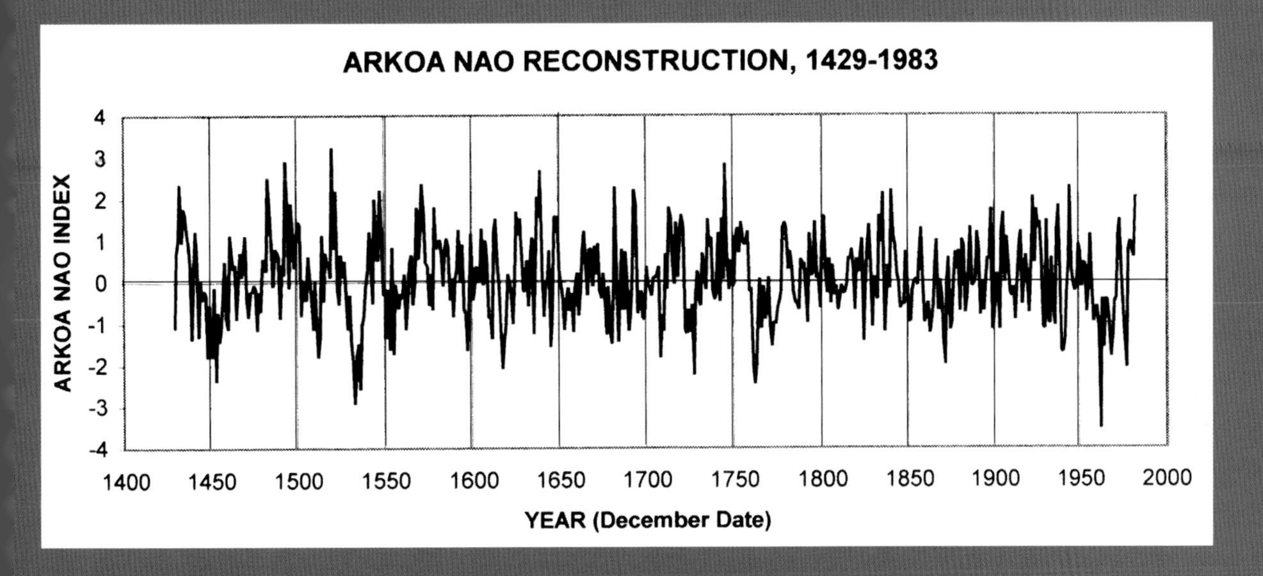

Reconstructed time series of NAO-index values going back into the Middle Ages.

which are closely connected to the NAO. The estimates are not really good enough to say whether Jardim do Mar was pumping when the Portuguese first landed on Madeira, or what Columbus's Atlantic crossing was like; but that wasn't really the idea.

More importantly, the time series is now long enough to seriously examine the *periodicity*; to find out how many of those embedded cycles there are; at what periods they occur, and which ones are the most important. The best way to visualize the periodicity of the NAO is to convert the 555-year time series into a *spectrum*. A spectrum is basically a graph that shows the most prominent cycles, and at what periods they occur (see figure at right). You can see that particular periods stand out more than others.

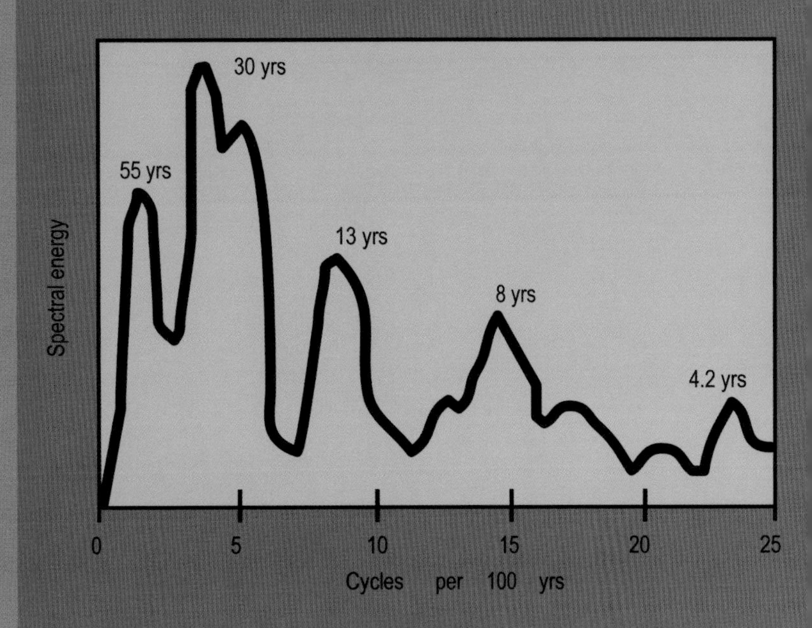

Spectrum of inferred NAO index, derived from data going back 555 years. Don't worry about the units – the most important feature is the peaks at 4.2-, 8-, 13-, 30- and 55-year periods, showing the length of the most important cycles in the NAO.

These appear as *spectral peaks* at 4.2-, 8-, 13-, 30- and 55-year periods, with the 30-year one being the strongest. That is to say, according to what has happened over the last half-millennium, and assuming that tree rings and ice cores are a good substitute for the NAO index, the strongest ups and downs in the NAO index seem to be every 30 years or so, with smaller ups and downs at 55, 13, 8 and 4.2 years, in that order. If we now combine this result with the assumption that wave heights in the North Atlantic closely follow the NAO index, we can stick our necks out a little further and suggest that particular features in the history of North Atlantic wave heights, such as the strong peak which occurred between the late 1980s and early 1990s, are most likely to repeat themselves at intervals of about 30 years.

With a high North Atlantic Oscillation index, you can expect to find surf like this along the coasts of Western Europe.

This conclusion suggests that runs of winters with big surf in the North Atlantic are most likely to repeat themselves at intervals of about 30 years, is based on a lot of assumptions. More importantly, it is also based on an *empirical* model; that is, a prediction of the future based on what happened in the past. It is not actually based on any real understanding of the physical processes that govern the behaviour of the ocean and atmosphere in the North Atlantic.

The NAO, just like any other atmospheric or oceanic phenomenon, is extremely difficult to predict, particularly in the short term, such as weeks or months. However, on longer time-scales, such as years or decades, it might actually be easier to predict. It seems that long-term patterns in the NAO are more heavily dependent on the circulation patterns of the ocean than on most other things. This simplifies any prediction models, allowing links to be made between the NAO and those sluggish, drawn-out changes in oceanic circulation. Some climatologists suggest that much of the really long-term variability of the NAO could be reconstructed from knowledge of the sea-surface temperature. They argue that the sea surface communicates its temperature to the overlying air, allowing it to control atmospheric characteristics like storminess over long time-scales. Other scientists have realized that the flow patterns of the ocean surface and those of the atmosphere are a two-way street – each one depends upon the other. Even simplifying it down to a minimum of interconnected factors, predicting the behaviour of the NAO is still bewilderingly complicated.

The North Pacific Oscillation

If the North Atlantic behaves in a 'see-saw' pattern, with alternating periods of 'blocking' and 'fluid' patterns, then it is logical to assume that the North Pacific does too. Well, it does, but due to its size, not quite in the same way. The Pacific counterpart to the NAO is called (not surprisingly) the North Pacific Oscillation (NPO). It has an index, called the NPO index, which works a little differently from the NAO index. The NPO index is defined as the pressure (sometimes temperature) difference between the Aleutian Islands in the mid-north of the North Pacific, and Edmonton in western Canada. The two points are displaced in an east-west direction rather than a north-south direction, as in the NAO index, and temperature is sometimes used instead of atmospheric pressure. Despite this, the index infers basically the same things: namely, whether there will be a large anticyclone off the west coast of North America (analogous to the 'blocking' pattern, with dryer, colder, less stormy weather and less surf), or strong westerlies hitting western Canada and Northern California (analogous to the 'fluid' pattern, with wetter, stormier weather and more surf).

In the North Pacific, unlike in the North Atlantic, whether one pattern or the other predominates depends strongly on the east-west position of a semi-permanent depression called the Aleutian Low. The position of this low can be inferred by the NPO index. Because the Pacific is so wide, it is the storminess in the eastern half of the ocean that principally affects the west coast of North America. If the Aleutian Low is in the western extreme – say, over the Sea of Okhotsk in eastern Russia – this will allow a large anticyclone to develop and lead to a 'blocking' pattern; but if the low is in the eastern extreme – say, over the Gulf of Alaska – this will allow strong westerlies to blow on its southern flank and lead to more of a 'fluid' pattern. Note that the NPO is also connected to the *El Niño* Southern Oscillation (see below).

The Arctic Oscillation

Some scientists argue that the NAO and the NPO can be amalgamated into a cycle involving atmospheric circulation in the entire hemisphere. The Arctic Oscillation (AO) is the cycle describing the general behaviour of both the North Atlantic and the North Pacific together. It is based on the premise that there is considerable correlation between both oceans. The AO index is typically based on the difference between the atmospheric pressure at the North Pole and the atmospheric pressure at mid-latitudes (about 45°N). If the pressure is abnormally low at the Pole and abnormally high at 45°N, the AO is 'positive', meaning more northerly storm tracks in both oceans, wetter weather in Alaska, Scotland and Scandinavia, and drier conditions in western North America and the Mediterranean. If the pressure is abnormally high at the Pole and abnormally low at 45°N, the AO is 'negative', with more southerly storm tracks, wetter, stormier weather in Western North America and south-west Europe, but drier conditions in more northern areas.

The Antarctic Oscillation

It seems that the Southern hemisphere has been somewhat neglected as far as wave-height climatology and long-term storminess are concerned. The Southern hemisphere has more water, more storms and more ships navigating in it, not to mention more surf spots than the Northern hemisphere. Ironically, the very same lack of

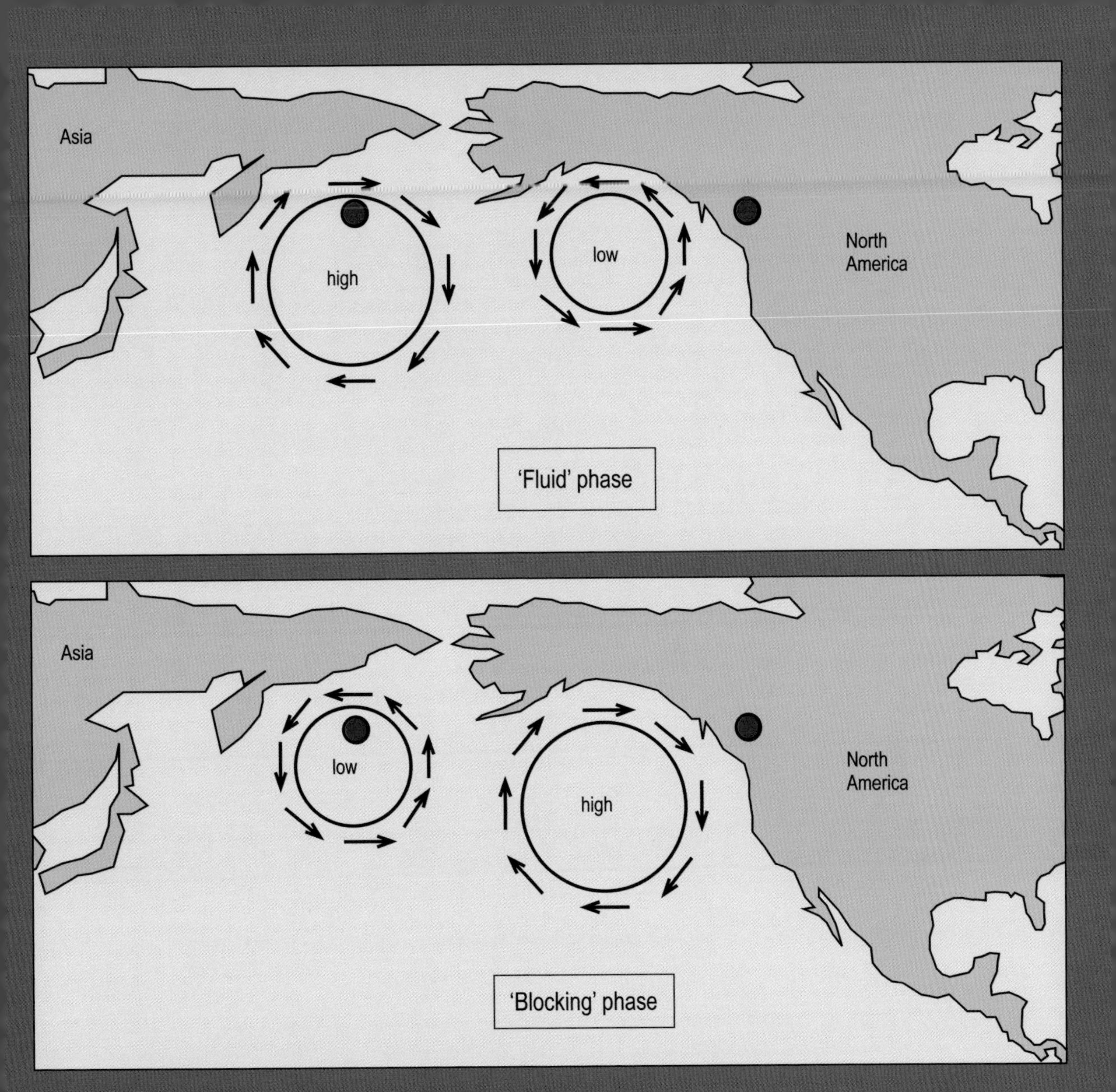

Schematic illustration of the two extremes of the North Pacific Oscillation, depending on the position of the Aleutian low. The two red dots are the measurement points for the NPO index. During the 'fluid' phase (top), the pressure is abnormally high in the west and low in the east; during the 'blocking' phase (bottom), the situation is reversed.

land means that the Southern hemisphere has less people and a smaller number of 'developed' countries, which might be why less importance has traditionally been placed upon it.

The land and sea in the Southern hemisphere are laid out very differently from those in the Northern hemisphere, and so the way they respond to atmospheric cycles is also quite different. This is important for us, as surfers, because there is a great deal of surf in the Southern hemisphere, with the ups and downs in storminess and wave heights affecting places like South Africa, South America, Australasia, Tahiti, Fiji and many other island groups in the South Pacific. The principal climatic cycle in the Southern hemisphere is the Antarctic Oscillation, or AAO. Just like the Northern-hemisphere cycles, the AAO can help us to understand the long-term ups and downs of the surf in the Southern hemisphere.

By looking at the map, you can see that the Southern hemisphere contains a lot more water than the Northern hemisphere. Travelling from east to west or from west to east in the Northern hemisphere, you wouldn't have to go very far before you hit some sort of land. In the Southern hemisphere, however, you could travel vast distances without meeting any land. For example, if you followed the 40°N line around the planet until you came back to the same spot, your journey would be split between about 44 per cent sea-crossing and 56 per cent land-crossing; if you did the same with the 40°S line, it would be about 96 per cent sea-crossing and 4 per cent land-crossing.

This difference between the two hemispheres is directly reflected in the climate. The westerly winds in the Southern hemisphere, which blow strongest at latitudes between 40°S and 50°S (hence the term *Roaring Forties*), are not interrupted by the presence of large land masses. In contrast, in the Northern hemisphere, the corresponding westerly winds are interrupted considerably by the great land masses of Eurasia and North America. Because the atmosphere behaves differently over the land from the way it does over the sea, the Northern-hemisphere westerlies always tend to be stronger in one place than another, while the Southern-hemisphere westerlies are distributed more evenly around the globe.

Consequently, scientists are able to consider the atmosphere in the Southern hemisphere as comprising of 'rings' around which the temperature, pressure and wind speed are similar. A large average pressure difference means strong westerlies, and a small average pressure difference, weak ones; the atmosphere 'see-sawing' between the two states. That may not seem particularly surprising, since the North Atlantic does just that. But, instead of see-sawing within a single ocean basin, as in the North Atlantic, the see-sawing is going on between two concentric rings encircling the globe. The oscillations in pressure of two rings around the Southern hemisphere, and the consequential strengthening and weakening of the westerlies at the latitudes between these two rings, is the AAO.

To express the current phase of the system within its cycle, an index can be derived for the AAO. The easiest way to define the AAO index would be to take the difference between the average atmospheric pressure around two rings at different latitudes. To make some sense out of the relationship between pressure and windspeed, the latitudes of these two rings would be chosen as being either side of the Roaring Forties – for example, 40°S and 65°S. Abnormally low pressure at 65°S, and/or abnormally high pressure at 40°S, means a large north-south pressure gradient, and hence strong westerlies; abnormally high pressure at 65°S, and/or abnormally low pressure at 40°S, means a small north-south pressure gradient, and hence weak westerlies. The crucial way this differs from the NAO is that the strength of the westerlies strengthens and weakens synchronously around the whole globe, and not just in one ocean.

Above, I described how values of the NAO index can be used as a rough proxy for wave heights in the North Atlantic. Can the AAO index be used in a similar way to infer wave heights around the oceans of the Southern

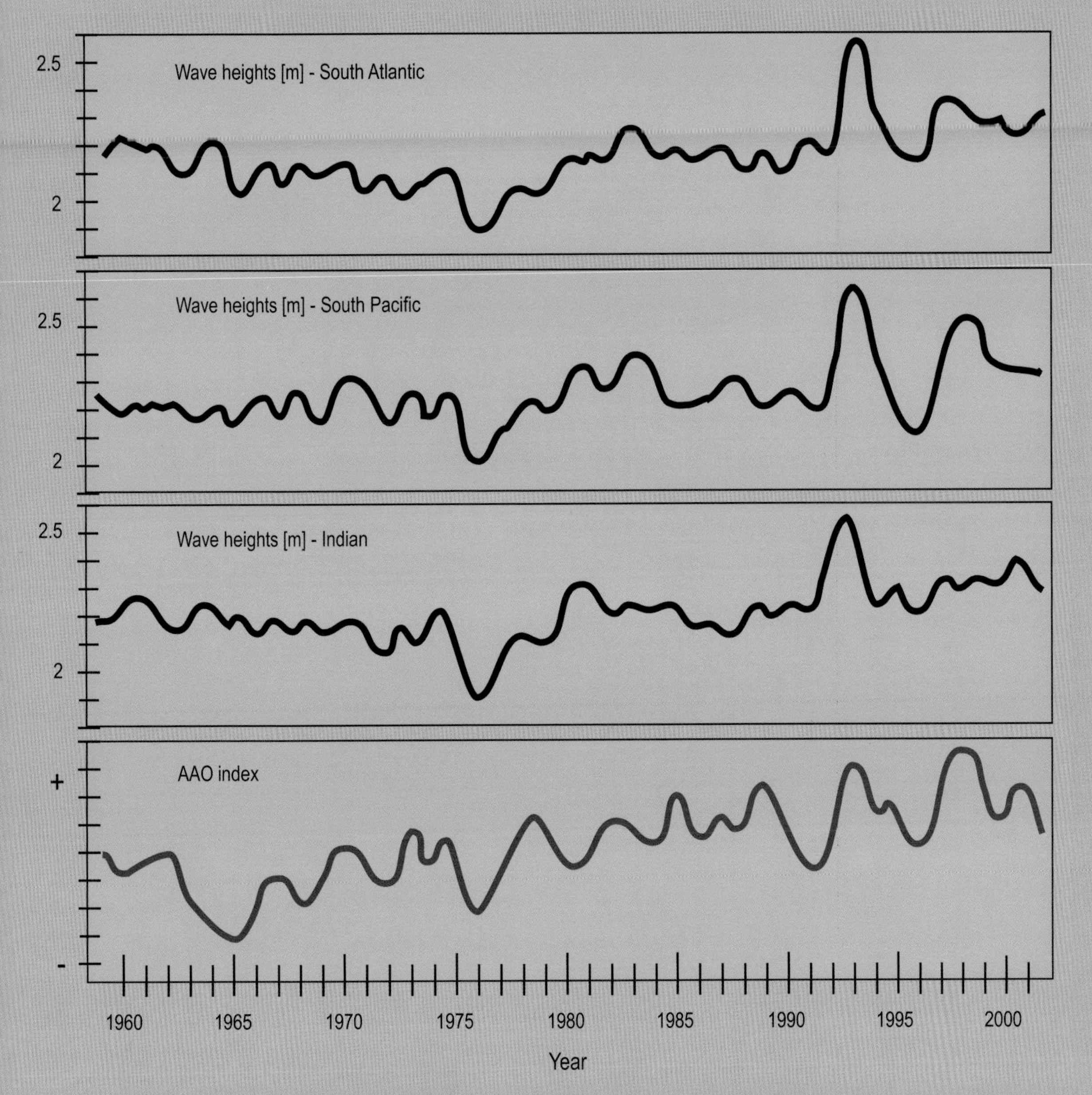

Time series covering the period 1961–2003. The top three, in black, are wave heights for the South Atlantic, South Pacific and Indian Oceans, respectively. The bottom one, in red, is the AAO index. The wave heights are highly correlated with each other, and reasonably well correlated with the AAO index.

hemisphere? Since AAO index values infer the strength of the Southern-hemisphere westerlies, it follows that they could also be used to infer wave heights. The way to test this is to compare a time history of AAO-index values with the corresponding time history of Southern-hemisphere wave heights. If the fluctuations in one roughly match those in

the other, then we can use the AAO index as a proxy for the wave heights, without actually having wave-height data.

The figure on page 61 shows some plots of wave heights for the Indian, South Atlantic and South Pacific Oceans, going back to 1961, together with a record of the AAO index covering the same period. The wave heights are spatially averaged over each ocean, and temporally averaged over the year. One thing that immediately stands out from the plots is that the wave height fluctuations in each ocean are remarkably correlated. Although the absolute values of the wave heights in each ocean are not exactly the same, they *do* go up and down more or less in sync with each other (big surf in the Indian Ocean means big surf in the South Pacific and big surf in the South Atlantic). This is very important, and is something you don't normally get in the Northern hemisphere. Another observation is that there are two major features on the wave-height plots: a big dip in wave heights around 1976, and a large peak in wave heights around 1993. Were these particularly bad and good years for surf in all the oceans of the Southern hemisphere?

If we now compare the wave heights with the AAO index, we can see that there is a reasonable correlation. The two major features on the wave-height plots – namely the 1976 dip and the 1993 peak – are also present on the AAO-index plot. There is also another peak in the AAO index at around 1998 which, curiously, shows up fairly strongly in the South Pacific and South Atlantic wave heights, but less so in the Indian Ocean wave heights. In summary, this simple exercise tells us that the AAO index can be used, albeit highly tentatively, as a single number to give a rough idea of whether wave heights were generally bigger or smaller than normal during conspicuous features such as those around 1976 and 1993. It can be used to predict ups and downs in wave heights, as long as those ups and downs are big enough to stand out considerably.

The *El Niño* Southern Oscillation

This chapter wouldn't be complete without at least a brief mention of the most well-known climatic cycle: the *El Niño* Southern Oscillation (ENSO), or simply the Southern Oscillation (SO). Although it originates in the tropical South Pacific, the SO has far-reaching effects all over the globe. It has been found to have a significant influence on storminess (and therefore wave heights) in the North Pacific, and hurricanes in the North Atlantic. The South Pacific ocean-atmosphere system fluctuates between two different states: *El Niño*, and its counterpart, *La Niña*. The cycle typically lasts between about three and seven years.

As with all the other climatic cycles, certain 'symptoms' are associated with each phase of the cycle. But first, it is helpful to understand the average or 'normal' conditions in the South Pacific (neither strong *El Niño* nor strong *La Niña*). The trade winds, which blow from west to east across the ocean, tend to 'pile up' the warm surface water in the western part of the South Pacific, principally around Australasia. The warm surface water heats up the overlying air in that region, making the air rise through the process of convection. Once that rising air reaches a certain height, the moisture it contains will start to precipitate out, forming large rain-bearing clouds and, therefore, rain. Meanwhile, on the other side of the ocean, along the coasts of Peru and Chile, the surface water is being blown away from the coast by the trade winds. This displacement of surface water allows the much colder water below to come up to the surface, which, in turn, cools the overlying air and puts a stop to any convection. No convection means no large rain-bearing clouds, and hence no rain, which is why the coast of Southern Peru and Northern Chile is the driest place in the world. The *upwelling* of cold water from below also means a constant supply of nutrients, making sure the coastal waters are teaming with life.

During the *La Niña* phase of the cycle, the trades are stronger than average, which reinforces the above set of conditions. The surface water piles up even more in the west, leading to warmer surface water in Australasia, more convection and more rain. At the same time, the upwelling of cold water in the east becomes stronger, maintaining the extremely dry conditions along the west coast of South America. During the *El Niño* phase, the trade winds are weaker than average, which reduces the piling up of the warm surface water on the western side of the ocean. Eventually, the warm surface water will gradually start to drift back towards the west coast of South America. The presence of warm water on the coast completely reverses the normal situation, leading to convection, clouds and rain in the desert. Meanwhile, in Australasia, the surface water is cooler than average, causing dryer-than-normal conditions. It is *El Niño* that is the more problematical phase for people, because, particularly in Peru, it tends to bring rain and floods in the desert, and shuts off the supply of nutrients from below in coastal waters, reducing the amount of fish available.

Most climatic cycles have an index to quantify whereabouts the ocean-atmosphere system is within that cycle, and the SO is no exception. The SO index is normally defined as the difference between the atmospheric pressure at Darwin, Australia, and that in Tahiti, about 8,500 km to the east. Under *La Niña* conditions, the pressure in Darwin is abnormally low, because the surface water (and, hence, the overlying air) around that area is warmer than average, leading to more convection, and more convection means a drop in surface pressure. Meanwhile, in Tahiti, the surface water is colder than average, meaning less convection and, hence, a rise in surface pressure. Under *El Niño* conditions, the situation is reversed, with abnormally low surface-water temperatures and

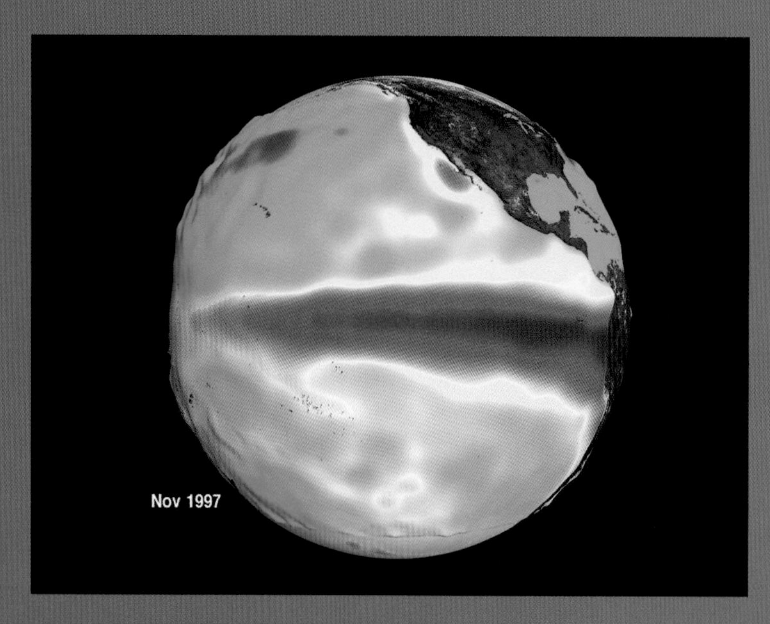

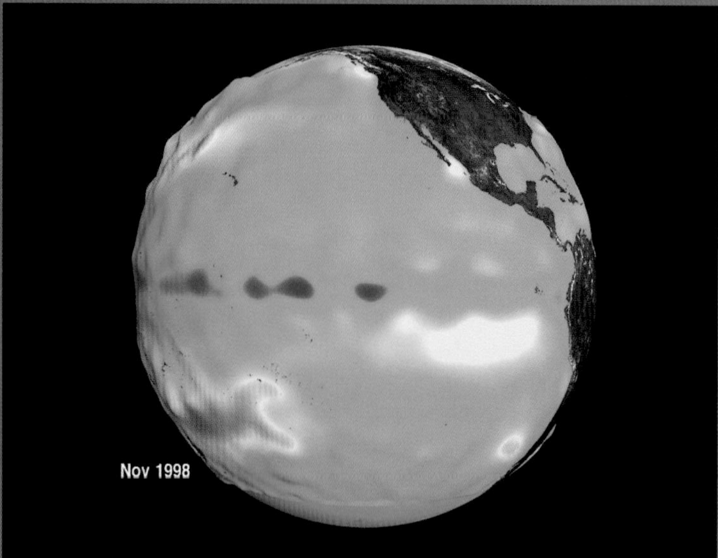

Representation of *El Niño* (November 1997, top) and *La Niña* (November 1998, bottom) conditions, derived from real data measured by satellite. Sea-surface temperature anomalies are represented as colours, with red being warmer than normal and blue being colder than normal. Sea-surface height anomalies are represented as exaggerated heights on the surface.

high atmospheric pressures in Darwin, and abnormally high surface-water temperatures and low atmospheric pressures in Tahiti.

But what has the SO got to do with oceanic storminess, and surf, if anything? Well, there is quite a lot of evidence that the track of mid-latitude depressions in the North Pacific is strongly influenced by the SO. The shifting from east to west, and back again, of the 'warm pool' in the tropical South Pacific has an effect on the upper air stream in the Northern hemisphere. The upper air stream – or jet stream – is what determines the trajectory of low pressures on the surface. It appears that, during *El Niño*, the jet stream in the eastern North Pacific tracks a lot further south than it does during *La Niña* conditions. This means that any mid-latitude depressions will also take a more southerly route across this part of the ocean. As a result, Central and Southern California will tend to receive bigger surf and stormier conditions. In contrast, during *La Niña*, the jet stream and, hence, the trajectory of mid-latitude depressions, tends to shift to a more northerly position, meaning bigger surf and stormier conditions for Northern California and western Canada. Note that recent research has found some correlation between the NPO and the SO.

Lastly, research has shown that the SO has some effect on the frequency and intensity of hurricanes in the North Atlantic. With strong *El Niño* conditions, the North Atlantic seems to experience a lower number of hurricanes and a reduction in strength of existing ones. One explanation for this is that, during *El Niño*, the upper winds in the western North Atlantic and the Caribbean are stronger, tending to 'chop off' the tops of tropical storms before they have a chance to form into hurricanes.

A complex system

After reading about the particular climatic cycles I've chosen here, you might realize that some of them are quite closely linked to others (the SO affects the North Pacific and is therefore linked to the NPO; or the NPO and the NAO can be amalgamated into the AO, etc.). In fact, they are all linked to each other, and they are also all linked to many other recognized cycles that I haven't mentioned here, some predominantly atmospheric, some oceanic, but most a combination of the two (therefore also demonstrating that the ocean is inextricably linked to the atmosphere). The climatic conditions on each part of the planet are unavoidably linked to those on the rest of the planet. The temperature and salinity of the ocean waters; the trajectory of ocean currents; the movement and extent of polar ice, river flow, rainfall; the behaviour of fish, mammals and other animals, including humans, and a huge number of other phenomena, are all intertwined in such a way that each one is dependent upon all the others. Also, with each type of oscillation operating over a whole spectrum of frequencies (the NAO might change phase every couple of weeks, but this is embedded in a seemingly infinite number of progressively longer cycles, with periods up to centuries or even millennia), how do we know that there isn't always a longer cycle? Unfortunately, we'll never know the true answer to that, although I'm sure it will continue to be a subject of great debate among scientists and philosophers.

5 Searching for the biggest waves

At 11:30 a.m. on 28 May 1953, Edmund Hillary and Tenzing Norgay reached the top of the highest mountain in the world, Everest. Their goal was well defined because Everest had long been known to be the highest mountain in the world, and was just waiting for someone to climb it. It would be absurd to think of a higher mountain appearing a few years later, and other climbers beating Hillary and Norgay's record. Ocean waves, however, are not like mountains. They are not fixed objects, but packets of energy that take the form of moving lumps in the water surface. So you can't really define the 'biggest wave in the world' in the same way as the highest mountain. Rather than being a stationary geographical feature like Everest, the 'biggest wave' is an event that lies somewhere in space and time. It follows that riding the biggest wave in the world, or even finding it in the first place, is much more complicated than climbing the highest mountain.

This chapter is all about the biggest surfable (including tow-surfable) waves; how big they can actually get; when and where they are likely to occur, and some of the things we need to know before embarking on a mission to find them. Using simple information on the climate of open-ocean waves, together with some of the basic principles of wave mechanics, we can learn something about finding the biggest waves. We need to know when and where these waves are generated; where they might break in a way they can be ridden, and what factors make or stop them being rideable. Even if you are not looking for the most massive surfable waves imaginable, looking for big waves in general is much harder than looking for small ones. Big waves are much more sensitive to conditions such as swell quality, swell direction, wind direction, tide, reef formation, and many other factors.

At present, the only type of wave that can be ridden on a surfboard is one that has been generated by the action of the wind blowing over the surface of the ocean – the wind-generated wave. So that's what I am going to talk about here: wind-generated waves, not tsunamis or waves generated by other processes – these have such long wavelengths and travel so fast that we cannot normally ride them, not even with the help of a waverunner.

In the storm

In principle, wind waves can be formed by any wind blowing along any surface of the ocean. This includes everything from weak summer sea breezes blowing over short sections of coastal waters, through moderate trade winds blowing constantly over tropical zones, to category-five hurricanes with winds of over 200 km/h. However, the only type of wind that has the potential to produce really huge waves is the wind that blows around a *mid-latitude depression* (those typical low-pressure systems you can see crossing the British Isles or the Pacific Northwest). You might think that hurricanes would produce bigger waves than mid-latitude depressions, since they tend to have much stronger winds; but hurricanes are small in area and fast moving, and their winds don't normally blow over a large enough stretch of ocean for a long enough time to generate really huge waves.

Of course, not all mid-latitude depressions are the same. Some generate much bigger waves than others, and this depends upon certain characteristics of the storm itself. The storm has the potential to produce the biggest waves if the windspeed, the *fetch* (the stretch of ocean over which the wind blows) and the duration (the length of time wind blows over that stretch of ocean) are all optimized. Whether or not that happens depends upon certain environmental factors that affect the storm throughout its life. For example:

- The storm must start off in a part of the ocean where atmospheric conditions tend to amplify storms. The best areas are just south of the northernmost areas of the North Pacific and the North Atlantic, and just north of the southernmost areas of the Southern Ocean. Then, usually only in that particular hemisphere's winter, do these storms occur.
- The storm must have plenty of area around it to maximize the fetch, but, at the same time, it must not encroach upon any land or ice during its swell-producing lifetime. If it does, it will lose energy.
- The water must be deep enough, so that the waves are not attenuated by the sea floor while they are being generated.
- Initially, the winds must blow at hurricane force or more for at least 12 hours over the same stretch of ocean.
- When the swell starts to propagate away from the storm centre, the storm should preferably 'chase' the swell, the wind travelling along synchronously with the swell it is producing. This ensures that energy is continually pumped into the swell.

Using mathematical models, research meteorologists have tentatively calculated that the maximum height possible for a wind-generated wave is about 67 m – inside the storm itself. But that's not really much use to us, because the waves we want to ride are not the ones inside the storm centre – they are too messy. The ones we're interested in are those that have propagated a fair way out of the storm centre and turned into clean swell lines. The size of those waves depends upon many factors, some of which reduce the original wave height, and some of which increase it. I'll say more about that in a moment.

The bigger the wave, the longer the wait

As we find ways of riding bigger and bigger waves, the waves we are looking for will be more and more difficult to find, and will occur less and less often. Logically, the bigger the wave, the longer you have to wait for it. This phenomenon has been studied extensively and for many years by scientists and coastal engineers, because it has direct applications for anyone who wants to build a coastal structure or modify the coast in some other way. They want to know how strong to build that structure to prevent it getting washed away within a specific time-frame. So they are interested in how often a wave of a certain height will arrive at their structure.

For each spot on the surface of the ocean there exists a *theoretical expected return time* for a wave of any given height. The expected return time is the length of time you must wait between successive occurrences of a wave of that particular height. To take a hypothetical example, a 1-m wave might be expected to occur at spot 'X' about once a week, but a 20-m wave might only be expected to occur there once every 100 years. At another spot, 'Y', a 1-m wave might only be expected to occur once every six months, and a 20-m wave may never actually occur. Scientists either obtain this information from statistical records of real wave heights at certain locations, or they predict it using mathematical models. For specific locations, graphs are often plotted showing how the expected return time increases as the wave height increases. Eventually, a 'limiting' wave height is reached: this is the height of the largest wave ever expected to occur at that particular location. By definition, that wave would occur only once in history.

But having a graph for each separate spot is a little tedious. Something more useful to us is the same kind of data, not for specific locations, but for areas covering entire oceans. This takes the form of a map showing areas where the waves are most likely to exceed a certain height within a certain time period. This kind of data does exist, usually in the form of a series of charts, each corresponding to a specific wave height. Each chart contains colour contours, each colour being associated with a number of days a year when the waves exceed that particular height. The figure on the left shows some charts of this type, compiled by scientists from the Royal Netherlands Meteorological Institute. The upper panel shows contours of the number of days a year that the waves exceed 5 m (the 5-m *exceedence*), and the lower panel shows contours of the number of days a year that they exceed 9 m (the 9-m exceedence). The charts were compiled using a technique called *reanalysis*. This is the use of computer models to generate large amounts (in this case about 30 years' worth) of past values of wave heights. Typically,

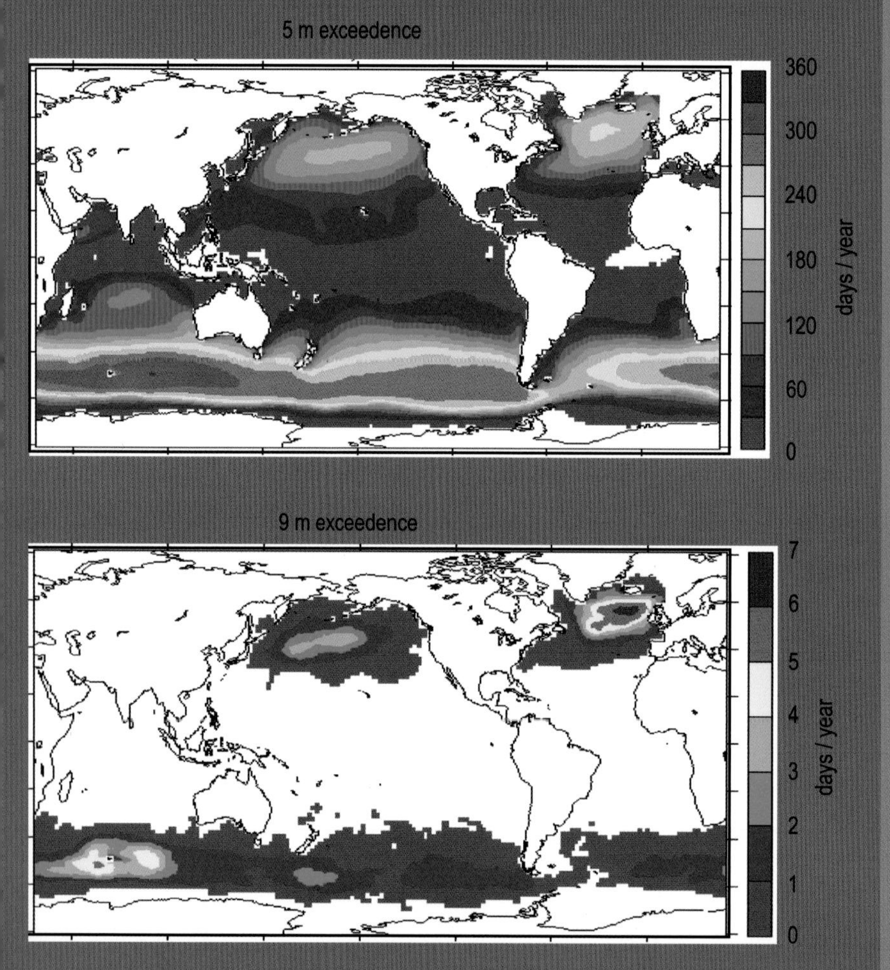

Upper panel shows the number of days per year that wave heights exceed 5 m. Lower panel shows the number of days per year that wave heights exceed 9 m.

atmospheric parameters such as pressure and temperature are compiled together to predict windspeed, which is then used to predict wave heights.

Looking carefully at the two charts, the results are quite revealing. In the top panel (5-m exceedence) we can see that, in the southern Indian Ocean just south-west of Australia, the waves exceed 5 m a staggering 300 days a year. In the North Atlantic, however, they only exceed 5 m about 200 times a year. So, if you want to surf consistent, medium-to-large waves, but are not particularly concerned about looking for that really huge day, then Western Australia is probably a better bet than Western Europe. If we now look at the lower panel (9-m exceedence), we see that the number of days a year when the waves exceed 9 m is greatly reduced in all oceans. Now it seems that the North Atlantic, with 9-m waves occurring six or seven times a year, has the edge on all other areas, including the Indian Ocean. Strangely, the North Pacific appears to lag behind both the Southern Ocean and the North Atlantic.

We all know that the North Pacific produces some of the biggest surfing waves on the planet, so, obviously, there must be more factors that we haven't taken into consideration.

Out of the storm

Waves inside the storm itself, deep ocean waves and rogue waves are not much use to us. The highly disorganized nature of waves inside a storm means that they are really just giant lumps that shoot up out of the ocean for a fleeting moment; they have no lefts or rights, and do not wall up or tube. Before we can begin to think about catching and riding these waves, we must let them propagate away from the storm centre for at least some distance on their own, 'freewheeling' without any further input from the wind. They then have the opportunity to organize themselves into clean lines, and eventually find a place to break left and/or right.

Knowing where the biggest waves are born, and in which direction they are likely to travel, is a good starting point. In the storm centre the waves are a confused mix of many heights, directions and wavelengths, all interfering with each other. But once the waves start travelling away from the storm, they are influenced by a process called *radial dispersion*, which I will explain very briefly. As they start to separate out, the longer, faster waves start to get ahead, and the shorter, slower ones start to lag behind. At a point some distance away from the storm centre, the first waves to arrive are those with the longest wavelengths, followed by those with slightly shorter wavelengths, and so on until the slowest, shortest-wavelength ones arrive. This is clearly better than having them arrive all at once, all mixed up together as they were in the storm. In fact, the very-shortest wavelength waves might not even get there at all. Being a lot weaker than the rest, they sometimes end up being attenuated to virtually nothing by things like opposing winds in the propagation path.

Another important factor which influences the surfability of the swell is the *directional spread*. If the waves are coming in from all directions, they interfere with each other and create a much more messy sea than if they are all coming in from the same direction. A point further away from the storm centre receives swell from a more limited range of directions than a point very close to the storm centre. This is because, closer to the storm, the 'window' through which waves can reach that point becomes narrower as the point gets further away from the storm(see diagram on page 70).

So, the further away from the storm centre the waves propagate, the cleaner and more rideable they get. However, at the same time, they tend to suffer a reduction in height as they spread out over a progressively wider area of the ocean. This process is known as

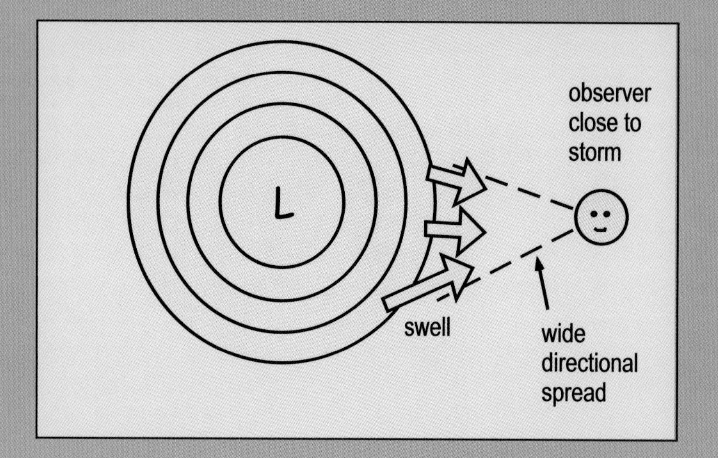

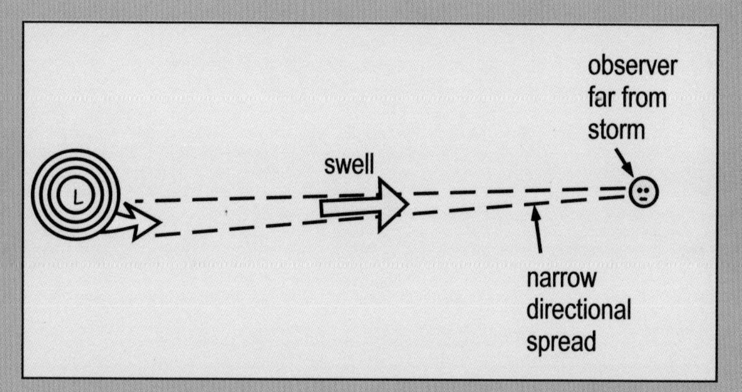

An observer situated close to the storm (upper panel) will experience swell from a greater range of directions than an observer situated a long way from the storm (lower panel).

distance at the expense of wave height.

So, in principle, just on the periphery of the storm itself, the waves have the greatest chance of being really huge, but they also have the least chance of being rideable. A long way from the storm centre, the cleanest and most rideable waves occur, but they are never as big as those in the storm. The ideal distance from the storm centre to find the biggest rideable waves would therefore be some intermediate point between where the waves are really huge but unrideable, and where they are rideable but not big enough. In other words, we need to find the closest spot to the storm centre where the waves first start to become clean enough to ride (see diagram at top of page 71). Examples of real areas around the world that might contain these sorts of places include, in the Northern hemisphere, Hawaii, Central and Northern California, Spain and Portugal; and, in the Southern hemisphere, South Western Australia, western South Africa, and Chile.

But what about places like Puerto Escondido in Mexico, which is a huge distance from the storm centres, but which can produce some of the biggest makeable tubes in the world? Well, there are one or more factors that work to re-enhance the height of swell waves, sometimes a long way after they have left the storm. As waves start moving into shallow water, just before they break, local refraction and shoaling effects can concentrate the wave energy into a limited area. This can sometimes restore the waves to the same height or even higher than they were in the storm itself, even if they have propagated a long way. I'm not going

circumferential dispersion, and can easily be understood if you think about a single wave crest propagating out from a point. We can even use the classic example of a pebble being thrown into a pond. As the circular wave crest expands away from the point where you threw in the pebble, the circle gets bigger and bigger. The wave is 'freewheeling' from the start – in other words, it does not receive any more energy than the initial energy given to it by the stone. Therefore, as it expands, it must share that energy over a wider and wider wave crest, 'stretching' the energy over a greater

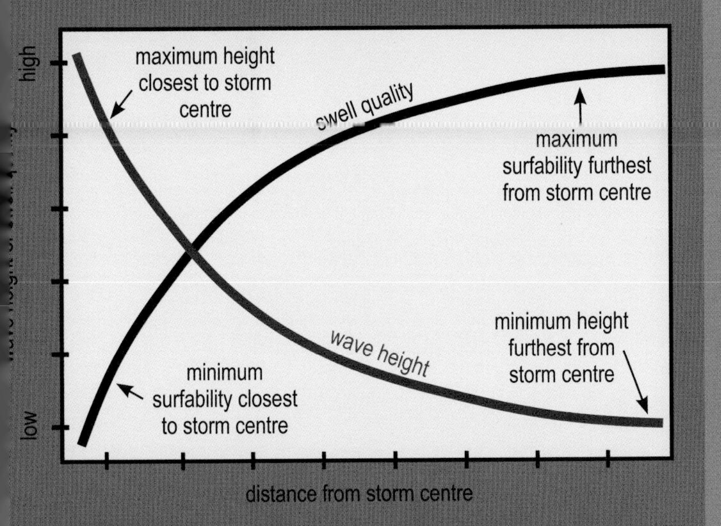

As the waves propagate further away from the storm centre, the 'surfability' increases but, at the same time, the height decreases. For big, rideable waves, the trick is to find the best compromise between the two.

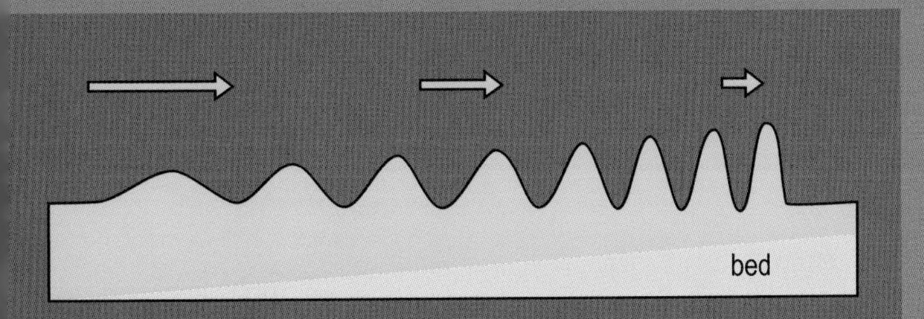

Exaggerated example showing effects of shoaling on a wave train propagating into shallow water. Note how the waves get higher as they slow down. Arrow length = wave speed.

to go into this too deeply, since I dedicated an entire chapter to it in a previous book, *Surf Science*. However, I will outline the basic reasons why wave heights can be re-boosted like this.

First, there is the effect of shoaling (see diagram above). This tends to enhance wave height significantly, especially if the waves suddenly hit a shallow reef out of deep water. Sometimes, just before a large wave breaks at a spot like Maverick's, where the wave comes out of deep water and hits a very shallow shelf, you can see how the front face of the wave suddenly grows, jacking up to almost double its size. As the waves start to propagate into shallower water, they start to 'feel' the bottom, and hence slow down. Logically, the waves at the front of a group hit shallow water first, which means that they slow down while the ones at the back of the group keep going at their original speed. This effectively squashes up the wave group, bringing the waves closer together. Squashing them up closer together tends to make them higher. If you can't see why this is, just take a piece of string, put it on the table, and put some waves in it. Then squash up the piece of string from one end to the other. The waves in the string should get higher.

Second is a mechanism called *concave refraction* or *bathymetric focusing* (see diagram on page 72). This is where the middle of a wave front starts to propagate over shallow water while the parts either side of it keep going in deeper water. The middle slows down but the outsides do not. As a result, the wave bends into the area of shallow water, rather like light being focused by a lens. This tends to concentrate the wave energy on to a peak, making the wave higher and more powerful. Extreme refraction can be seen at places like Jaws, where the deep-water swell height can be magnified to at least twice its height by the focusing effect of a shallow reef with deep water either side of it.

Both these mechanisms are powerful ways of re-enhancing wave heights far away from the storm centre. One other factor that makes these mechanisms even more effective is that they work better on waves with longer wavelengths. The further away

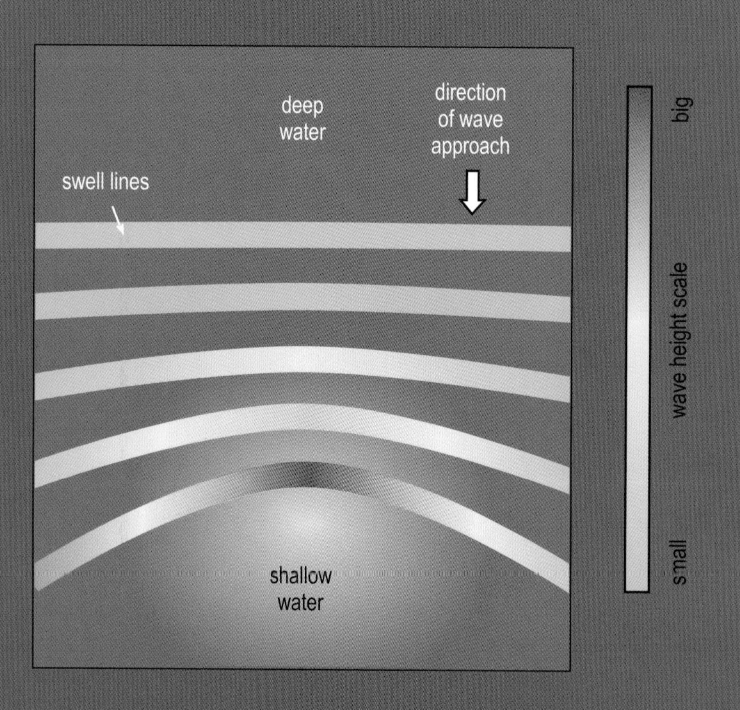

Bathymetric focusing on to an area of shallow water. The middle of the wave slows down relative to the outsides, concentrating the energy and increasing the wave height.

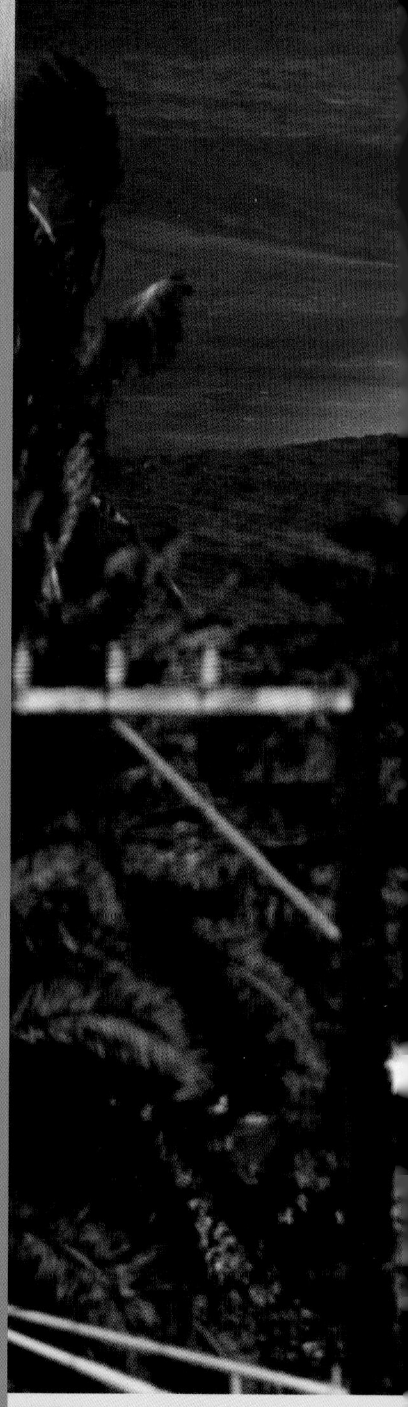

from the storm centre the waves propagate, the more the longer, faster waves outpace the shorter, slower ones, due to radial dispersion, as I have just explained. Therefore, at places where the waves have propagated a long way from the storm centre, particularly at the beginning of a swell when the longest-wavelength waves start to arrive, the re-enhancement of wave height due to shoaling and refraction is at its maximum.

One swell-enhancing phenomenon that doesn't really concern waves for riding but, nevertheless, is fascinating, is that of *wave-current interaction*. This occurs out in the open ocean, normally where the waves have already started propagating away from the storm centre and have formed fairly well-defined swell lines. If there is a strong current flowing into these rolling swells from the opposing direction, it will pump energy into the swells, piling them up steeper and higher, similar to the shoaling effect described above. As a result, huge swells are magnified to humungous proportions. For example, just off the coast near Durban, South Africa, where the south-westerly flowing Agulhas current flows head-on into the huge swells coming up from the Southern Ocean, there are frequent

Sunset Beach, Hawaii. The North Shore of Oahu is close enough to the storm centre to receive large swells, yet far enough away that the swells arrive clean.

observations of waves over 20 m high. In some areas of the Agulhas current, the water is less than 100 m deep. This is easily shallow enough to cause some kind of focusing of these gigantic waves, possibly contributing further to their regrowth. To actually break in 100-m depth, the waves would have to be at about 80 m high.

When the waves break

Finding a spot with the right local sea-floor contours (*bathymetry*) for giant waves to break suitably for riding, is just as vital as identifying the areas where they are generated in the first place. Apart from the shoaling and refraction effects described above, another very important factor is how big the waves can break over the reef without closing out. For a wave to peel either right or left, there must be a considerable variation in depth in the direction perpendicular to the direction of wave propagation (in coastal areas, this is called the *alongshore depth variation*). Logically, the water must be deep enough on at least one side of the reef for the wave not to break there. Most, although not all, surfing reefs can only hold up to a certain size wave without closing out. This is because, generally, the part of the reef containing the alongshore depth variation extends only a certain distance offshore. Beyond that, the depth contours run parallel to the coast. If the waves are big enough to break this far out, they close out. If not, they continue on to the inner part of the reef, where they peel right or left.

We can illustrate this with a simple example (see diagram on page 75). According to the most basic wave theory, waves break where the depth is about 1.25 times their height, on average. But to keep things even more simple, we will assume that they break when the depth is equal to their height. In the diagram, the waves are approaching the

A wave breaks over the bow of the *Esso Nederland II* in the Agulhas Current. The bow of the ship sits about 25 m above sea level.

shoreline from the top towards the bottom of the picture. There is an alongshore depth variation nearest the shore (bottom of the picture), which fades out with distance until the depth is about 6 m, where it disappears all together (top of the picture). Imagine a wave, say 3 m high, propagating down from the top of the diagram. This wave will break when it hits the 3-m depth contour, about half way down. It will not close out, but will instead form a right-hander that peels along the 3-m contour, towards the bottom left of the diagram. Now, imagine a 6-m wave. This wave will break as soon as it hits the 6-m contour at the top of the diagram. Since this contour is straight and perpendicular to the wave approach, the wave will close out.

So, the trick is to find somewhere where the 'close-out' depth contour is really deep. Using some excellent animated graphics, a handful of the world's most famous big-wave spots were described by Sean Collins in the film *Making the Call*, together with their 'close-out' depth contour, to illustrate just how big a wave these spots can hold without closing out. One that differs from all the others is Cortes Bank, situated about

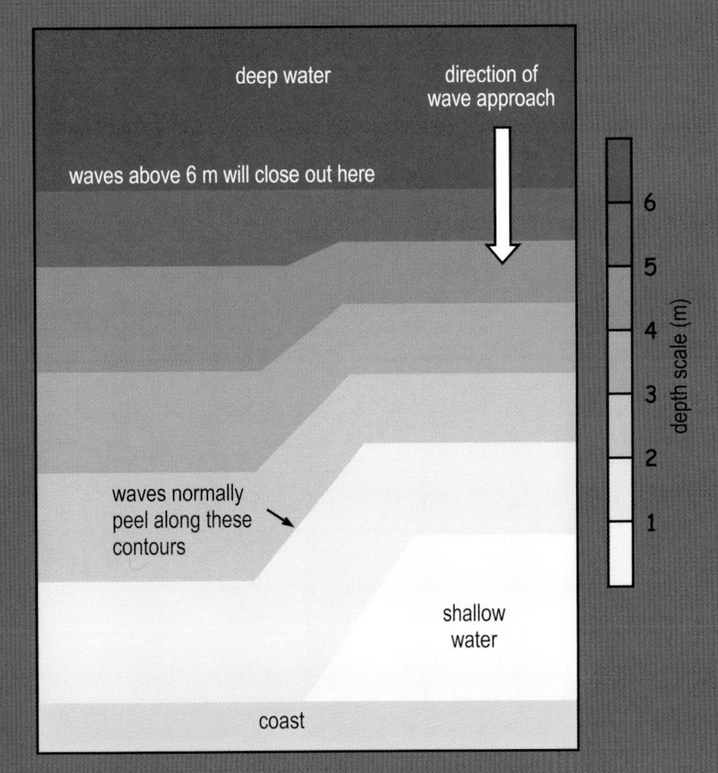

Hypothetical chart of coastal depth contours. Waves smaller than 6 m high will not break in the channel on the left-hand side of the diagram, which means they will form a right-hander peeling along the depth contours. Waves of 6 m or more will close out on the 6-m depth contour at the top of the diagram.

170 km west of San Diego, California. Being an offshore shoal, surrounded by water that quickly drops off to depths of well over 100 m, Cortes Bank is practically unlimited in the size of wave it can hold.

The wind

Then you have the wind. The face of a big wave needs to be clean if it is to be ridden, and that means calm conditions or very light winds. In big waves, especially those that break a long way from the shore, any wind is a hindrance. A slight offshore wind is magnified up the face a thousand times, making the chops bigger than the waves most of us surf at home. A side or onshore wind does not make things much better, either. Therefore, another factor to take into consideration when looking for places that hold big rideable waves is the wind regime. At latitudes closer to the storm centres, in addition to the fact that the waves themselves are usually too mixed-up to surf, there are fewer days in the year with favourable wind conditions. Even a considerable distance from the storm centres, areas exist where trade winds and local effects also generate undesirable winds. The least windy areas (near the Equator) are not that useful either, because they are simply too far away from the storm centres to ever have really big waves. So, probably, the spot that can hold the biggest rideable waves in the world is in an area where the wind regime is highly variable – where a few hours of calm conditions can appear at any time in between rapid changes in direction and sudden increases in strength. Once the spot has been chosen and the swell arrives, all you then have to hope for is a couple of hours of windless conditions.

First-ever session at a recently discovered spot on the north coast of Spain. With nothing with which to compare the waves from the cliff top before going out, the two surfers seriously underestimated the size.

6 Controlling the waves: every surfer's dream?

Big-wave riding is an amazing thing to do. It is addictive but healthy, scary but relatively safe, and you never stop learning. But big-wave riding nowadays also means big business. All around the world, professional surfers, their managers and their photographers are constantly at the ready, prepared to fly anywhere to get the 'big shot'. To ride and get photographed on the wave that measures the most from top to bottom can mean big fame and big dollars. It would be nice to believe that every big-wave rider and every towsurfer does it *only* for love and definitely *not* for money, but this just isn't true.

Nowadays, big-wave riding and towsurfing go far beyond the act of riding the wave. That 'afterglow' – once a sensation enjoyed only in the mind of the rider, privately thinking about and reliving that wave for some time afterwards – can now mean tangible things like money and fame. After every session, it is now important to go over all the photographs, measuring the height of the wave against the surfer just in case it might be a contender for this year's $50,000 award. There is no doubt about it, the image of a person standing on a board with a huge, blue wave behind him is highly photogenic, and the managers of clothing companies have realized that using these images for advertising is a great way to sell their product. Contest organizers have also realized that a successfully run big-wave event can be spectacular. Whether all this is good or bad in the long run, I'm not going to speculate. Like most things, it probably has its good points and its bad points.

One reason why this is happening at the moment might be because the technology is now available to put people on bigger waves than ever before. The sport of towsurfing has opened up the possibility of accessing what was once known as the 'unridden realm' – waves over 8 m high like those on the outer reefs in Hawaii. For years, surfers tried every way they could to catch these waves using paddle power, but they never really succeeded. Now, with a waverunner to tow the rider in, and a tiny, narrow, heavy board with footstraps, the 'unridden realm' is no more. Towsurfers can ride bigger waves than they ever dreamed of. In fact, the biggest waves able to be produced on this planet (wind-generated, not tsunami, as I pointed out in the previous chapter) are probably not too big to be towsurfed.

In the previous chapter I also stated that, as we start looking for bigger and bigger waves to ride, the more difficult they will be to find. At each particular spot, we will have to wait longer and longer as the size of the wave we want increases. Eventually, surfers and towsurfers will start coming close to the limit; each time the record for the biggest wave is broken it will be more and more difficult to find a bigger one. In fact, the sensation of missing it, not quite being in the right place at the right time (perhaps within a matter of hours) will be felt more and more, and there will always be a wave a little bit

Practising on an early prototype reef.

bigger, unridden and with nobody there to witness it.

Contest organizers are also going to find it increasingly difficult. To go one better than the last time the event was held, with bigger and cleaner conditions, will be harder and harder. Audiences will start to get bored if the contest isn't more and more spectacular each time. Big-wave contests are already put on hold, sometimes year after year, if conditions aren't big enough and clean enough. It is always tempting to hold the event anyway, even in marginal conditions. Big-wave contests are logistical nightmares, sometimes requiring quite a few days' notice to organize things like the press and international competitors. Conditions are also so difficult to forecast that big-wave contests are sometimes held on the wrong day, or cancelled just hours before the waves become epic.

So, what if we could skirt around all those problems by actually *manufacturing* the waves we want, when we want? After all, they already make artificial reefs, so why not artificial waves? Well, in the near future, people just might try to make this happen. Of course, artificial swells of the sizes needed cannot be produced in some giant wave pool, they are simply too big. So we are going to have to generate them 'naturally' but with a little human help; we are going to need to modify the weather itself. In this chapter, I'm going to look at deliberate anthropogenic weather modification, and how it is still being thought of as a possibility, despite the

The Chronicle

JANUARY 20, 2025

Boom! The boat shudders as another huge wave explodes on to the sandbag reef. The audience are fixated on a spot a little further out to sea. The rider, hardly perceptible in the distance, moves his back foot over the pressure pad to switch the mini-jet into semi-overrun mode. He must keep the power on; otherwise the friction between the board and the water will not allow him to reach the bottom of the wave. Just before he eases a bottom turn, he waits until the wave has jacked up behind him and the lip has begun to throw out. At that moment, the photographers shoot like crazy, each one covering a different angle. The wave, estimated by the reef's electronic transducers to be some 72 m high, makes a sound that easily drowns that of the five helicopters. The surfer runs along the middle of the wave, pulls out and meets the service team. They tow him back to the boat as number-two rider checks his life jacket and oxygen bottles, starts his mini-jet, and heads out to the line-up.

The specially designed reef, lying about 2,000 km west of Guayaquil, Ecuador, focuses the huge waves generated by the North Pacific Permalow into well-defined rights and lefts. It is one of 13 such reefs in the Pacific Ocean, each with a slightly different set of characteristics, purpose-built to be ridden by the jet-board riders competing for the Goodman Challenge. The reefs are positioned in equatorial or tropical zones, far enough away from the Permalow to allow the gigantic swells to clean up. These areas also tend to have favourable natural wind conditions, which saves on expensive local weather-modification systems.

In the past, any type of sport that relied on the weather conditions being right was always going to be limited in its commercial success. Now, thanks to the Storm Adjustment and Redirection System (SARS), put into use as part of the Global Climate Control Program, huge waves in bright, sunny weather are available for every event in the Goodman Challenge. Needless to say, jet-board wave riding now attracts multi-million dollar sponsorships and is becoming as popular as football or formula-one motor racing was at the beginning of the century. Each event in the Goodman Challenge is broadcast on live TV in over 500 countries worldwide, with an estimated audience of over 2,000 million. Immediately after the event, hologram podcasts are available for download, both from a spectator's and surfer's eye view. There are 13 separate events, held annually between the months of December and March, one at each reef. The overall winner is the rider who has been photographed on the biggest wave after all 13 events have been held. He normally gets around $10 million.

The Goodman Challenge is named after research meteorologist Derek Goodman. Goodman was the first to calculate all the characteristics required to generate the biggest possible waves from a mid-latitude depression, and is the inventor of the North Pacific Permalow. The American-owned Permalow is a low-pressure system designed to 'idle' over the ocean under normal circumstances, but which can be adjusted at short notice according to requirements. The US Air Force, responsible for the maintenance and running of the low, has granted special permission for its winds to be increased for the Goodman Challenge. The low is 'cranked up' for just long enough to produce the colossal swells necessary for the 13 one-day events. Unidirectional pulses of swell are generated over one-day periods, with giant waves calculated to arrive at the reef in question during the hours of the event. Although the waves in the generating area are precisely controlled, those breaking on the reefs tend to vary in direction and size. This tests the skill of the rider, his jet-board designers and his photographers.

obvious fact that we are not even close to understanding the climate of this planet.

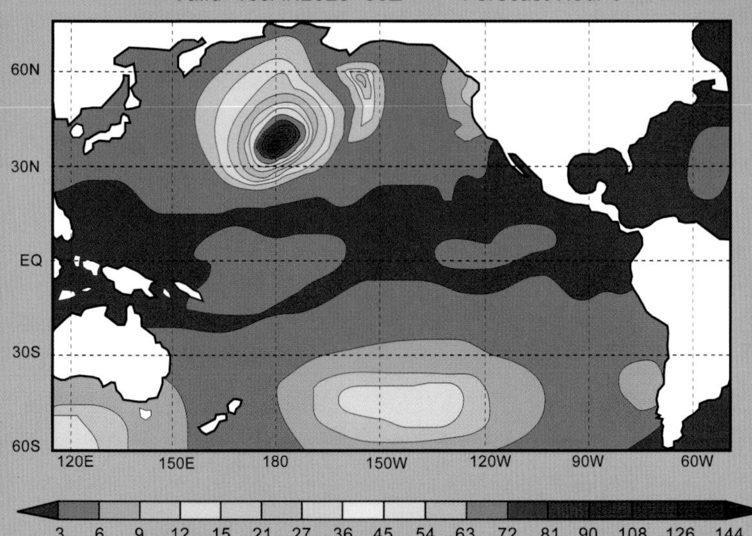

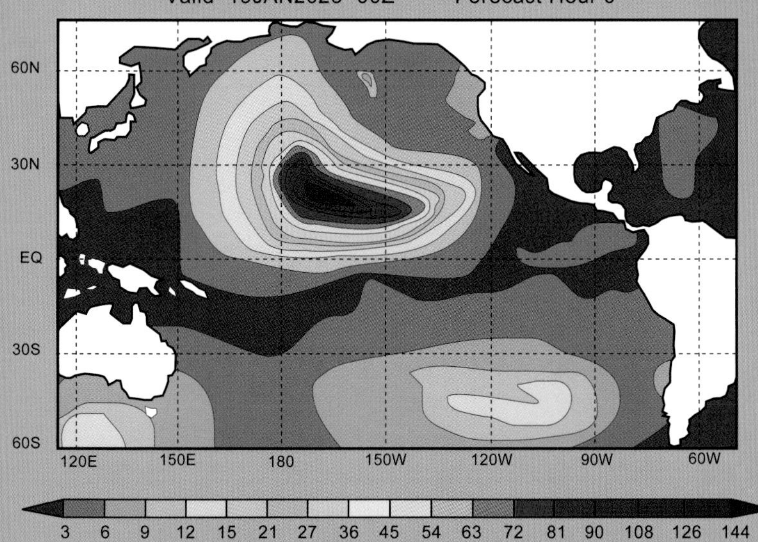

Upper panel: Wave-height 'nowcast' chart of the Pacific Ocean from Fleet Numerical and Oceanographic Center, showing the Permalow. Lower panel: The Permalow gets cranked up for the Goodman Challenge.

Obviously, the absurd vision of the future depicted in the article on the opposite page will never come true, and anyone who ever gives it a thought must be out of their minds, right? Well, perhaps not. According to some scientists, an artificially generated low pressure is not beyond the realms of possibility. It seems the potential advantages of being able to control the weather are just too tempting to resist investigation. Research into weather modification is actively going on.

Even if such a radical thing as the Goodman Challenge didn't ever take place, the surfing advantages of weather modification could still be incredible, couldn't they? After all, with the recent popularity of artificial reefs, the surfing community is already used to the concept of 'custom' surf spots; so why not 'customize' the waves themselves? Imagine if, say, the swell could be turned on and off like a tap, and if local wind conditions could be precisely controlled. No more wasted journeys to the beach, and no more days off work for nothing. Being a slave to the surf-prediction websites would be a thing of the past. We could choose when and where to surf, not just according to the type of beach or reef that suits us, but also according to the wave height we wanted. There could be a cater-for-everybody scheme, where different wave heights would be generated on different days of the week – 2 ft on Mondays, 5 ft on Wednesdays, 12 ft on Fridays, for example. We would never again have to surf with nasty onshore winds or wrong swell directions. And the benefits to contest organizers and sponsors would be tremendous, wouldn't they?

The idea of weather modification is not new. Rain-making rituals, where people believed that performing some kind of dance or song dressed up in elaborate costumes would make it rain, have been practised since the beginning of society. The desire was always there to control our weather, although, for thousands of years, our own influence on the elements remained negligible. It was not until the end of the Second World War that all that changed, and scientists began to think seriously about actively interfering with the atmosphere. Most of the interest was still in making it rain, particularly using the technique of *cloud seeding*. This is where chemicals are released into the atmosphere to trigger the condensation of water vapour and the formation of droplets. The droplets then grow until eventually they become too heavy to stay up there, and fall out as rain.

Over the next 30 years or so, there was a great deal of research and experimentation into weather control, and a few more bizarre forms of weather modification were considered. For example, once scientists realized that we were already inadvertently modifying the climate by pumping greenhouse gases into the atmosphere, it was postulated that, in theory, we should be able to do the same thing but in a more controlled manner. Another incredible scheme was proposed by Russian scientists in 1956, whereby the Bering Strait would be dammed up and cold water would be pumped out of the Arctic and into the Pacific. This would suck warm Atlantic water into the Arctic, melt all the ice and make the Artic navigable. Siberia would be nicely warmed up in the process, too. US presidential candidate John F. Kennedy suggested that the idea might be worth exploring as a joint research project with the Russians.

That idea was talked about until the early 1970s, when the US government was spending more than $20 million a year on weather-modification research. Just after that though, people started to become suspicious about the ethics of weather control, especially after a secret rain-enhancement experiment in Vietnam (which failed anyway) had been revealed to the public. A series of resolutions were put forward against weather modification for military purposes. This culminated in a United Nations international convention against hostile use of environmental modification techniques, which finally came into force in 1976. From then on, research into modifying the weather for our own benefit was put on the back burner. It was considered too difficult, too risky, and ethically questionable.

Fast-forward to the early twenty-first century, and a new generation has started to be tempted into rejuvenating weather-control research. Once again, the world's top military brains have started to ignore both the potential human and the environmental problems associated with weather modification. A comprehensive report by the US Department of Defence was released to the public in 2002, explaining how the US military will continue to '... dominate the atmosphere and space in the year 2025'. One section, entitled 'Weather as a Force Multiplier: Owning the Weather in 2025', deals with how they intend to modify the weather for military purposes. The report starts as follows: 'In 2025 US aerospace forces can "own the weather" by capitalizing on emerging technologies and focusing development of those technologies to warfighting applications', and contains statements such as: 'The potential benefits and power are extremely lucrative and alluring for those who have the resources to develop it', and: 'The tremendous military capabilities that could result from this field are ignored at our own peril.' According to the report, the overall grand plan is split up into various sub-strategies, each one having a specific military use. These include: precipitation enhancement or denial; storm modification or enhancement; cloud and fog generation, and space-weather modification. This last one is where the ionosphere – the outer layer of the Earth's atmosphere – is interfered with in order to alter the propagation of radio communications signals and, hence, confuse the enemy.

Ongoing research into storm modification is also taking place outside the military. One researcher at a private meteorological consulting company in Massachusetts has been investigating the possibility of modifying the intensity and propagation paths of hurricanes. Ross Hoffman, once a student of the legendary 'inventor of chaos', Edward Lorenz, has run computer simulations that suggest a hurricane could be sent off-course if the sea surface temperature were altered by a relatively small amount, in the desired direction. He has hypothesized that any weather system could be successfully modified, as long as one could find the minimum atmospheric change required – anything more than this and the system would go frantically out of control. He has been working on a program that will constantly measure the present state of the atmosphere, and continually look for the smallest changes required to nudge the system in the right direction.

It is easy to see why there is so much enthusiasm for this kind of project. By redirecting hurricanes, we could avoid billions of dollars worth of damage. Not only that, we could increase farming productivity and boost income from tourism by increasing or decreasing rainfall. We would enjoy an enormous list of benefits from being able to control our weather in this way. And of course, if hurricanes could be redirected and perhaps altered in their intensity, there is no reason why the same techniques might not be applied to a mid-latitude depression. Both these types of storms are what generate the surf we ride. So, once we can dominate them, we can dominate our surf.

That sounds great, doesn't it? But now let's have a closer look. To control the path of hurricanes, a practical way of modifying the temperature on selective parts of the sea surface must be found. One suggestion is to have giant mirrors to reflect extra sunlight on to the areas in question. The mirrors would be mounted on satellites. Another idea is to fill the sky with aircraft whose vapour trails would act as extra cloud cover, effectively cooling certain areas of the ocean's surface. If that didn't work, then the hurricane could be deprived of its energy by stopping water vapour evaporating from the sea. A thin film of oil would be sprayed on to the sea surface over an area covering a few hundred square kilometres, in the path of the hurricane, which would effectively impede evaporation, suck all the energy out of the hurricane, and slow it right down. Environmentally friendly organic oils have been experimented with, but results have been disappointing because the oil gets dispersed easily in choppy conditions. In contrast, synthetic oils tend to stick to the surface more readily, and so would be much more likely to succeed. If, after all that, the hurricane still refused to be shifted, then you could physically steer it in the desired direction using more persuasive methods – for example, creating an artificial wind, perhaps using offshore wind farms. Instead of using the windmills to generate electricity, they would be connected up in reverse, turning them into electric motors, with their rotor blades becoming giant fans. The power to drive them might come from small nuclear reactors.

Incredibly, most critics of the hurricane-steering project only seem to be worried that, once put into place and working normally, the scheme might lead to heavy lawsuits by one country against another, or even 'weather wars', triggered because altering the path of a hurricane might prevent loss of life in one country (the USA, for example) but cause the number of deaths to increase in another country (Mexico, for example). What they fail to realize is how absurd the whole thing is in the first place. Such a drastic attempt at interfering with nature would be riddled with unpredictable and undesirable knock-on effects. Since we haven't actually succeeded in reversing, or even slowing down, the negative effects caused by our current messing with the environment, a scheme that proposes spraying the sea with synthetic oil or installing giant mirrors in space is, to say the least, being rather hopeful.

It seems, after all, that the whole idea of weather modification, for whatever purpose – surfing, military, or otherwise – is fundamentally flawed. None of the simple experiments performed in the past ever really worked, and moral implications have been raised that ought to stop us trying again. Although technology is advancing at an ever-increasing rate, so is our knowledge about chaos theory and the interconnectedness of all physical systems on the planet. Therefore, we should realize that attempting to modify the climate could throw things irreversibly out of balance.

Let's look at what might happen if the Goodman Challenge went slightly wrong ...

The Goodman Challenge has been running successfully for five years. The North Pacific Permalow has been sitting there in its 'idling' state – designed to maintain perfect equilibrium with its surroundings – for nine months out of every year. Only between December and March is it purposely cranked up to super strength to produce the huge waves required. So far, the Permalow has not been used for any other purpose. And, so far, nothing weird seems to have happened to the climate.

Suddenly, under pressure from additional sponsors, the organizers decide to extend the Goodman Challenge for an extra two weeks, repeating events at some of the reefs. They obtain permission from the US military to turn up the Permalow from 80 to 90 per cent of its maximum capacity for six 15-hour periods during the following two weeks.

That particular year, however, one of the strongest *El Niño* events just happens to be taking place, with the principal effects being felt in the Pacific Ocean. *El Niño* is one phase of a natural cycle called the *El Niño* Southern Oscillation (ENSO). During this phase, a temporary weakening of the easterly trade winds which would normally maintain a 'warm pool' of water to the western side of the South Pacific, means that this water is allowed to flow back eastwards, eventually arriving at the coast of South America. A series of knock-on effects causes topsy-turvy atmospheric-pressure patterns, leading to rain in the coastal deserts of South America and drought in the jungles of Indonesia and Papua New Guinea. (More about *El Niño* in Chapter 4.)

By 'turning up the volume control' on the Permalow, artificially strong westerly winds are generated on the southern flank of the low. These winds encroach on to northern parts of the North Pacific high-pressure system, where, this particular year, the easterly trade winds are already very weak. This brings those trades to a virtual standstill, and, in turn, enhances the effects of *El Niño*, pushing things over a threshold and causing a cascade of progressively more severe knock-on effects. The entire planet's heat-transport system is suddenly thrown irreversibly out of balance.

In the space of a few months, the pressure over the entire tropical rain belt has increased so much that rainfall has virtually ceased there. Huge forest fires rage uncontrollably over Northern Australia and Indonesia, and start to spring up in Central Africa and South America. The fires continue to burn for several years, gradually but permanently depleting oxygen levels in the atmosphere. The smoke from the fires blankets out the sun. Eventually, the Earth is pitched into a dark, cold, perpetual winter.

Within 20 years, prime production has virtually come to an end. Within 40 years, most surface life has died, including humans. During the next few centuries, the planet adjusts itself to a different state of dynamic equilibrium, unable to support the type of ecosystem that humans were once at the top of. Small, anaerobic micro-organisms, previously banished to living below the mud and in people's stomachs, rise up and dominate the Earth for the next 60 million years.

After the 2029 Goodman Challenge, things started to go seriously wrong with the climate.

Coastal Intervention

In this section we look at some of the ways in which the coastline is modified by us humans, and why we must be careful in doing so. In some cases it is unavoidable: for example, ports and harbours are essential for transporting most of the stuff we consume every day. But in other cases, such as when coastlines are urbanized by greedy developers, or when poisonous chemicals are introduced into coastal waters, the damage done to the natural environment could be avoided. As a surfer, you'll probably be more aware of this than other people, whether through the sudden appearance or disappearance of a good surfing wave due to some coastal structure, or, perhaps, through the effect on your surfing experience of a change in the cleanliness of the water.

The first chapter explains a little about coastal erosion, why it is happening and why people generally don't like it. Some coasts are naturally eroding as a part of the ongoing metamorphosis of the planet, but others are eroding due to something we have done. Although our knowledge about coastal change is improving all the time, we still often make mistakes. Sometimes, for example, you find coastal structures designed to reduce erosion problems in one place creating even worse problems in another place.

The second chapter is specifically concerned with the effects of man-made coastal structures on surfing and surfing waves. Sometimes we benefit from these schemes: many urban surf spots around the world wouldn't be there if it weren't for a pier, breakwater or sand-dredging operation. But, unfortunately, most of them tend to have a negative effect on the surf, with a number of world-class breaks having been recently destroyed or degraded.

The third and last chapter in this section delves into chemical, rather than physical modification of the coastline, looking at oil spills and the way they have affected coastal populations, including surfers. We compare two cases from both ends of the time-scale: the *Torrey Canyon* from 1967, and the more recent *Prestige*, from 2002. Finally, we look at a couple of studies showing how large contamination events such as these can seriously interfere with the ecosystem.

7 Coastal erosion

John is not worried about coastal erosion. The biggest thing on John's mind at the moment is building a dam and stopping that river. He can't think about anything else. The possible knock-on effects of John's dam – the reduction in sediment supply to the nearby beach, leaving it wide open to increased erosion from the next storm, and the potential loss of beachside property – are beyond John's comprehension, because John is a beaver.

Obviously John's dam is so small that its long-term effects on the environment are not going to be very great, and they are not going to significantly affect the lives of other beavers. In fact, the effects of John's dam are a necessary part of the dynamic equilibrium of the natural world. But if John had bulldozers, concrete and money, like we do, things might be different.

This chapter is not about beavers, it is about humans – creatures clever enough to invent bulldozers, concrete and money, but sometimes not clever enough to realize that nature is our friend, not our enemy. We are clever enough to alter the natural environment to suit our short-term needs, but not always clever enough to manage those changes properly. As a result, the long-term detriments often tend to outweigh the short-term benefits.

One example of this kind of environmental mismanagement is the various methods we have invented for protecting the coastline against erosion caused by storms and large waves. This is not as simple as it may seem, and very often ends up causing unforeseen complications. In some cases, sophisticated coastal protection schemes temporarily solve problems in one place, but result in the need for more schemes to solve newly created problems somewhere else.

The coastlines of the world are slowly changing anyway – all part of the natural transformation of the planet. It is all changing – the climate, the biology, the shape of the continents and, logically, the shape of the coastline. Some coasts are in a state of advance, and others are in a state of retreat. In some cases, this coastal movement is part of a cyclic system, where coastlines are alternately eroding and accreting but with no long-term change; in other cases, it forms part of the continued systematic reshaping of our continents. Whichever the case, the coastline is changing, and it is doing so in a controlled manner. This is called *dynamic equilibrium*.

The problem with us humans is that we like our environment to be static, not dynamic. We expect the natural environment to remain the way it is after we have built hotels, houses, roads, shopping centres and, sometimes, whole cities, right there on the coast, and expect the coast to stay still. When it starts moving, we panic. So then we build even more concrete structures, like sea walls, groynes and breakwaters, to stop the coast eroding and causing damage to the human habitat we have built there. If we are lucky, these schemes will do what they were designed to do, but they very often end up causing further erosion problems which turn out to be more difficult to deal with than the original ones. Sometimes it ends up being a never-ending battle, like trying to patch up a leaking roof with chewing gum.

What I have just described above is summed up by the famous quote of

Salinas, northern Spain – a beach with excellent waves and a nice sea wall to protect several high-rise tower blocks built virtually on the waterline.

G. Soucie, from an article published in the *Smithsonian* in 1973:

> The real conflict of the beach is not between sea and shore... but between man and nature. On the beach, nature has achieved a dynamic equilibrium that is alien to man and his static sense of equilibrium. Once a line has been established, whether it be a shoreline or a property line, man unreasonably expects it to stay put.

If you surf, you are going to spend more time on the coast than almost anybody else, so you are going to be highly sensitive to coastal modification in the form of concrete structures, especially if they end up affecting the waves we ride. Of course, surfers also exploit the coast, but I'd like to think we do it in a more 'sustainable' way than most. I'd like to think that we are quite happy most of the time keeping the coast in its natural state, and that we don't see the need to 'develop' it with shops, cafés, bars, hotels, car-parks and houses, just to enjoy it.

Why is the coast eroding?

In places where the coast is eroding, and we consider it a 'problem', it is useful to think about *why* it is eroding in the first place. Several factors are responsible, some 'natural' (they probably would have happened if we weren't here); some obviously caused by us, and some a combination of the two.

One thing that is causing a systematic coastal retreat is the fact that the sea level is progressively rising. This is due to two factors, both linked to the steady increase in the Earth's temperature. The first of these is the melting of the continental glaciers, which adds water to the ocean; the second is simply that water expands slightly as it gets warmer. These two processes have combined to make the water level increase by about 15 cm in the last century. Much of this can be attributed to a 'natural' global temperature rise associated with a very long-term cycle. Now, thanks to the fact that we are pumping greenhouse gases into the atmosphere, the rate of temperature rise is expected to increase, which could greatly increase water levels, especially through glacial melting.

The natural occurrence of storms, particularly hurricanes, is something that causes sudden, episodic erosion of coasts. These events often take coastal dwellers by surprise – they react as if Nature has turned against them and something should be done about it. Well, most of the time, storms hitting the coast are a normal and necessary part of the existence of our living planet; they only become a 'problem' if people put themselves and their property on a coastline that is likely to receive these storms. So we could say that coastal erosion from storms is normally completely natural but, if we choose to let it affect us, well, that's our own fault. However, there is now some evidence that the strength and frequency of hurricanes and mid-latitude storms are increasing due to global warming. If this is the case, then we are not only causing ever-greater problems for ourselves because every Tom, Dick and Harry wants to live ten metres from the shoreline, but we are exacerbating the problem by making the storms themselves worse. Of course, in many developing countries, millions of people didn't choose to live on the coast or in low-lying areas. If global warming is intensifying storm activity, then many of the erosion problems being faced by millions of people in coastal areas of poor countries are a direct consequence of over-consumption by us in the so-called developed world.

In some areas, one of the major contributing factors to the dynamic equilibrium of the beach is the constant supply of sediment washed down to the coast from inland areas via rivers and streams. The beach may rely on this sediment supply to replenish the sand washed away by the action of the waves. Making sure that the supply of sediment from the land is not interfered with has been greatly overlooked in the past. Once a coastal area has been covered in houses, shopping centres, roads and car-parks, the natural flow of sediment from the land to the coast may be greatly inhibited.

The construction of dams can also greatly hinder the coastward flow of sediment. The Aswan Dam on the River Nile, for example, has been the indirect cause of extensive erosion along the Nile Delta in Egypt, where the coast has been retreating at up to 200 m a year. In contrast, other kinds of interference can cause a disproportionate increase in the sediment supply to the coast, leading to silting up of estuaries and ports, and then further intervention by ourselves as we try to remove this extra sediment by dredging. For example, in the Huanghe River in China, extensive forest clearing has led to huge increases in the amount of sediment being picked up and transported downstream by the river, which has resulted in the rivermouth becoming hugely silted up.

Over geological time-scales, the coasts of the world are constantly adjusting themselves as the tectonic plates drift around over the surface of the planet. Scientists have categorized coasts as being in a state of advance or a state of retreat, according to the movement of the tectonic plates. For example, 'collision coasts' like the west coast of North and South America, characterized by mountains, cliffs and a narrow continental shelf, are the result of the ongoing collision between continental and oceanic plates. These coasts have a high occurrence of earthquakes and seismic activity, and tend to be retreating (in other words, eroding). 'Trailing-edge coasts', like the east coast of North America, characterized by dunes, offshore islands and a wide continental shelf, are nowhere near a tectonic boundary. These coasts tend to be advancing, partly due to a large amount of sediment being drawn from long-flowing rivers coming all the way from the mountains on the opposite side of the continent. This kind of coastal adjustment is entirely natural and, as far as we know, not influenced at all by human activity.

The last thing I'm going to mention here is entirely of our own doing. It is brought about by a coastal modification scheme put in place by us – usually some concrete structure sticking out into the sea which interferes with the natural currents and sediment transport along the coast. Sometimes these structures are put there to protect previously built structures from being washed away due to coastal erosion. This is a situation that could easily wind up in an endless feedback loop of causing more problems by trying to fix a previous problem. The best thing to do is not start in the first place.

Why is coastal erosion a problem?

Coastal erosion causes problems on every scale: from the catastrophic erosion caused by huge storms hitting coastal settlements built on fragile wetlands or barrier islands, to the slow narrowing of a tourist beach over a number of years. One important thing to realize is that coastal erosion might have been caused by some factor from another time or place. Many people already live in low-lying cities or countries, where recent coastal erosion problems are not necessarily due to their own actions. They might have been caused by somebody from a previous generation having built some structure which, for some reason, is only now starting to cause problems; or they might have been caused by somebody in a faraway land changing the global climate and making the sea level rise.

In some places, however, people continue to build expensive beachside properties, hotels, car-parks and walkways, right on the coast, and then complain when the sea comes and washes them away. Many people also fail to see the coast and beach as anything but another kind of money-generating 'resource'. If the beach suddenly starts to become narrower, it will hold less money-spending tourists; this means there will be less income from the local shops, bars, hotels, restaurants and car-parks. In fact, in some tourist resort areas such as the Costa del Sol in Spain, or the Gold Coast of Australia, a dollar income rate has been attached to each square metre of sand surface on the beach. For the people who control the businesses in these places, coastal erosion is a major threat to their pockets.

Lastly, there is the fact that coastal erosion might affect the waves for surfing. Some surfers probably just think of the coast as a natural resource to be exploited for our own entertainment. But a lot of others are genuinely conscious of the fact that the best way to exploit it is in a 'sustainable' way, by altering it as little as possible. I would also like to think that many surfers find the inevitable natural changes to the coastline easier to accept, and are therefore much more tolerant of those natural changes. For example, most surfers are quite used to short-term changes such as shifting sandbars in summer and winter, after long flat spells or after big storms. Rather than being a hindrance, many surfers would say that this makes surfing beachbreaks more interesting. In the longer term, surfers rarely suggest that some structure should be built to mitigate the systematic erosion of a beach through natural causes, even if it means that their waves are disappearing. But surfers do tend to get annoyed when coastal erosion occurs due to a coastal modification scheme built for some other purpose, especially if we consider that purpose unnecessary, and it also threatens the waves.

Options to avoid being affected by coastal erosion

If coastal erosion is a problem for you, then you will have thought about how to make it less of a problem. There are many choices, most of which come under the 'active' category. These include structures designed to try to stop the sea coming in and causing coastal erosion – the so-called 'hard' options – or schemes where the material eroded from one part of the coast is replaced by 'grafting' coastal material (usually sand) from somewhere else – the so-called 'soft' options. All these schemes effectively modify the environment to accommodate our own behavioural patterns. Some choices, however, are based on modifying our own actions to work around Nature. These come under the 'passive' category. Passive choices are a little more difficult for people to swallow, and are based on the assumption that coastal erosion is going to happen anyway, whether or not we are here. They include just letting your million-dollar coastal property get washed away, or perhaps moving it inland to somewhere more sensible. The best option would be prevention rather than cure. In other words, a proper coastal zone management scheme that is fully aware of future coastal erosion problems, and so stops people building there in the first place. There is a whole continuum of sub-categories in between each of these schemes, and I'm not going to go into detail about every single one. I'll just describe some of the most common examples, together with their intended

(1) Beach being eroded by alongshore sediment transport.

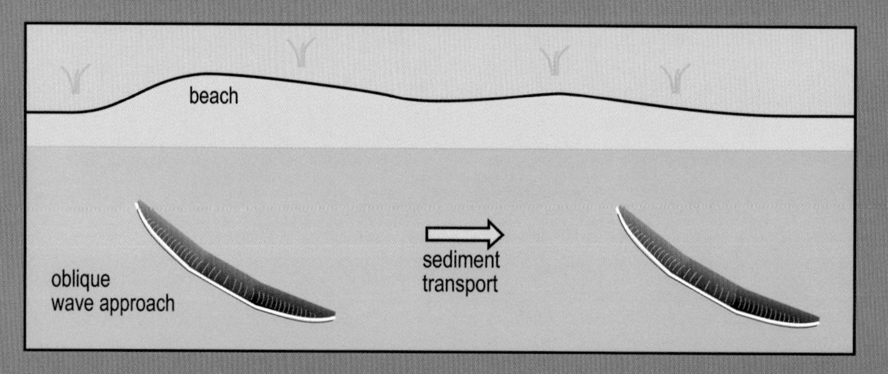

(2) After groynes installed, beach widened on upstream side of each groyne.

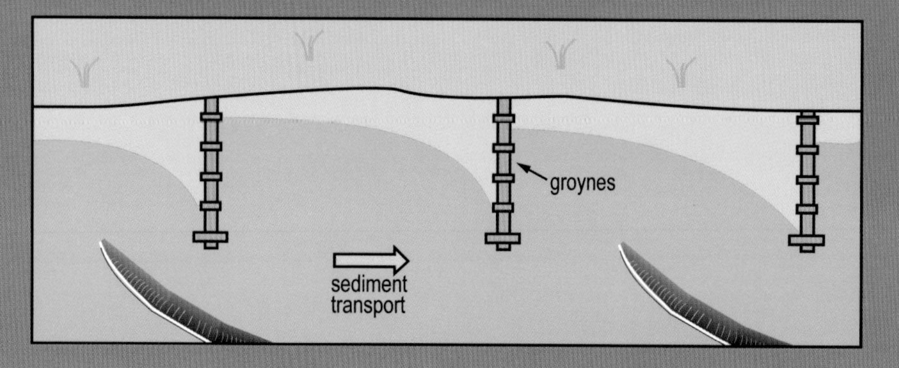

On a stretch of beach where the waves typically come in at an oblique angle, groynes are a good way of trapping sand that would normally be transported along the shore.

purpose and typical side effects.

The so-called 'hard solutions' are the crudest form of coastal protection. They include structures such as harbour walls or breakwaters, which are normally built to stop the wave energy entering a specific area such as a commercial port or a yacht harbour, but can also be put just offshore of a beach to stop the waves coming on to that beach and eroding it away. Then there are sea walls – structures built along the coastline to protect, say, a row of houses or a walkway when the beach that had been protecting it starts to get eroded away. There are also groynes – a series of wooden or concrete walls built perpendicular to the coastline, as illustrated in the diagrams on page 92. These are used in places where there is an oblique wave approach on a fairly lengthy stretch of coast. They are sand-trappers, interfering with the sediment-carrying currents that flow along the shore, thus allowing the sediment to build up on the upstream side of each groyne. This keeps the beach wide enough to contain a few more money-spending tourists.

(1) Coastal property in danger of being washed away by natural erosion.

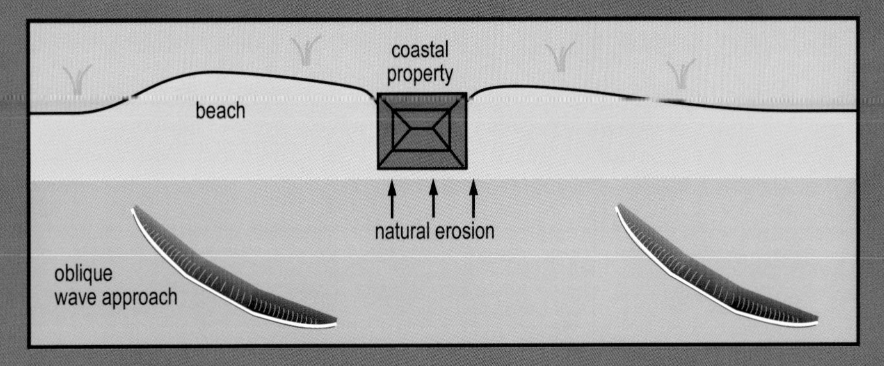

(2) Sea wall protects the property, but causes erosion at adjacent beach.

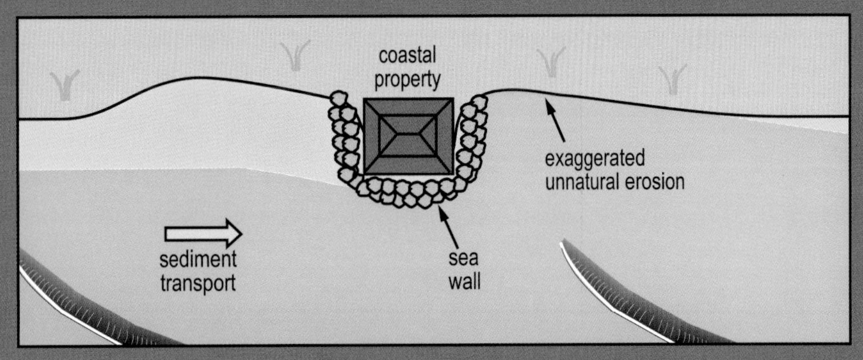

A sea wall built around a property that protrudes into the waterline may result in severe erosion downstream of the property.

What you have to watch when installing these structures is that the sediment supply isn't suddenly cut off at some part of the coast downstream of your 'territory'. In fact, a sea wall built around a property right on the waterline can act as a kind of giant groyne, if you're not careful. After erosion has taken place either side of the property (but not at the property itself because of the wall), if there is an oblique wave approach and the sediment transport is along the shore, there will be accretion on one side and severe erosion on the other side, as in the diagram above. People using the beach on the eroded side might not be too pleased about this.

Don't forget, natural beaches remain in equilibrium through natural inflows and outflows of sediment. Each particular section of beach could be thought of as having a sediment inflow and outflow, or a source and sink. If the source and sink both have the same rate of sediment transport, then everything is all right; but if the source is suddenly blocked off for some reason (for example, somebody has dammed up a river which supplies sediment to the coast), less sediment will flow

(1) Sediment flow into and out of cell is same, hence no erosion.

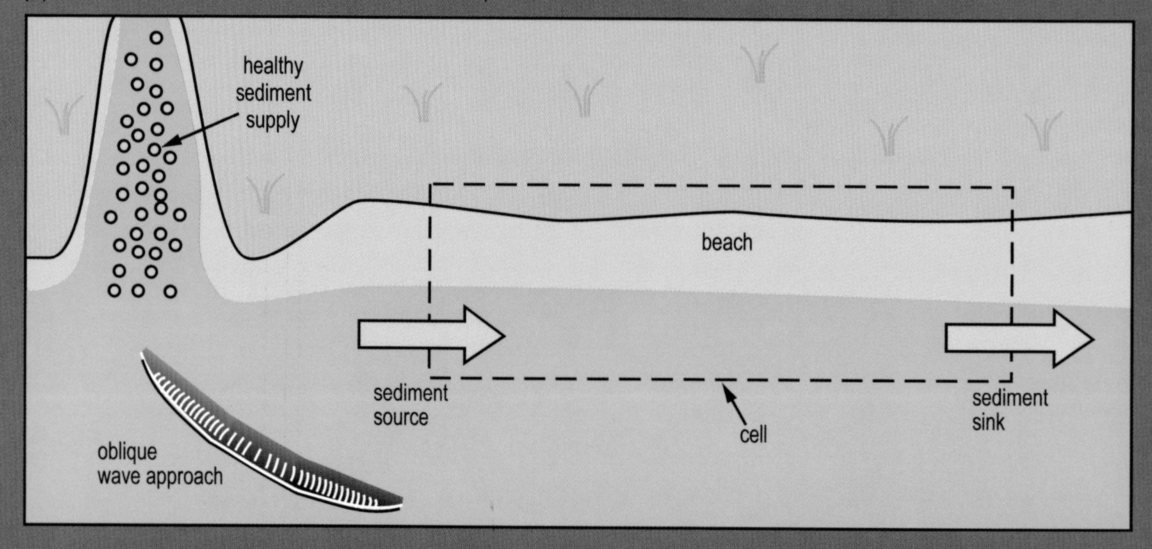

(2) Sediment inflow less than outflow, hence erosion inside cell.

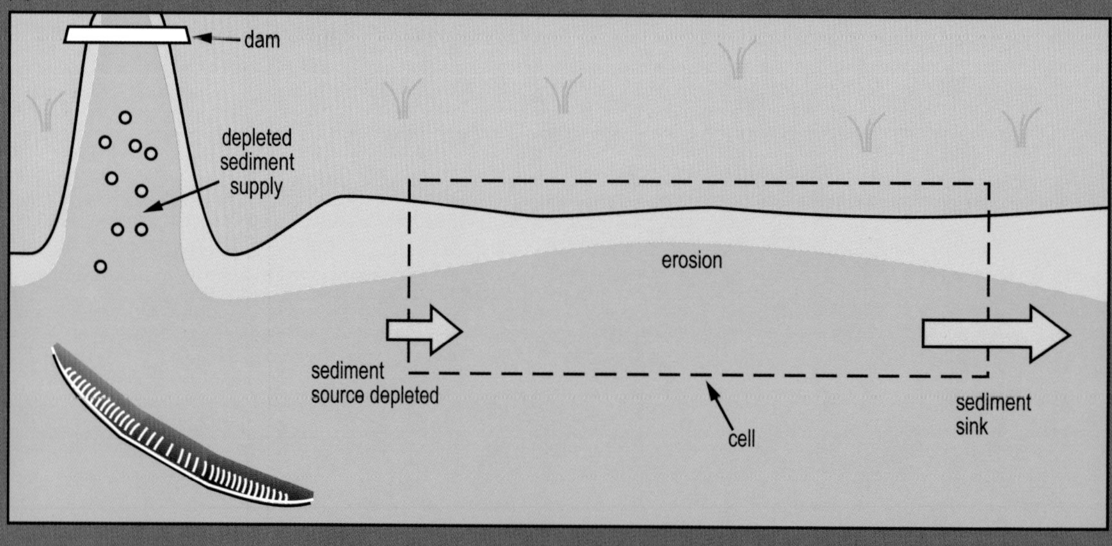

To understand erosion from alongshore currents, a section of beach can be thought of as a 'cell' with sediment inflow and outflow (source and sink). If the source is blocked off, the inflow will be less than the outflow, resulting in erosion at the cell.

into the section than out of it. As a result, that section of beach will experience a sediment 'deficit', and will end up being eroded. This is explained in the diagram above.

A typical breakwater that could be found anywhere in the world. This one happens to have a good surfing wave nearby.

Nowadays, people are realizing that hard structures can sometimes do more harm than good, and in some places are actually designing them to fail in the event of a large storm. In Florida, USA, for example, hard structures are designed to withstand the force of only a small storm. The idea is that, if a sea wall, for example, survived a huge storm, but the coast either side of it was eroded away, the wall itself would then end up right in the middle of the breaking waves, which would cause even more interference to the natural currents and sediment transport.

A slightly more ingenious idea for protecting people's coastal property is the 'submerged breakwater', or artificial reef. This is a permanent structure, but it doesn't stick out of the water – a 'semi-hard solution'. If you put an artificial reef just offshore in an area with a small tidal range, nobody can see it. They are cheaper than groynes or breakwaters and, if you can design them to be just the right shape to hold a good left and right, even better. Artificial reefs kill two birds with one stone, from two different points of view. On the one hand they are coastal protection structures that can be used for surfing, and on the other hand they are artificial surfing reefs that also happen to serve as coastal protection schemes. Many proposals for artificial reefs have failed because they have been put forward as purely for surfing purposes. The idea seems a lot more attractive to members of a local council if they are told its principal function is not for surfing, but for coastal protection – in other words, to protect those valuable beachside properties, often owned by the council members themselves.

An alternative to building a hard or semi-hard structure to stop the coast getting washed away is a 'soft option', such as a sand renourishment or bypass scheme. This is where an existing beach is artificially widened or maintained against natural erosion by bringing in millions of tonnes of sediment from somewhere else. The sand is usually obtained by dredging it up from an area of deeper water. It might be a one-off operation whereby the sand is brought in by

Detached breakwaters at Sea Palling on the east coast of England. The sand promontory joining the shore and the breakwater is called a tombolo.

truck or ship and dumped on to the target beach, often accompanied by some hard structure, such as a groyne, to keep the sand in place. Or it might be an ongoing affair, whereby sand/water slurry is pumped in giant pipelines from one site to another, with the volumetric flow rate being continually adjusted to compensate for the natural response of the coast. One problem with sand renourishment is that the site where the sand is being taken from must be able to withstand having all its sediment 'robbed'. If it is an estuary or other complex system, the consequences could be highly chaotic. Another problem is that, even if accompanied by some structure to keep the new sand in place, the sand often ends up disappearing anyway.

The Tweed River bypass system is a sand renourishment scheme on the Gold Coast of Australia, which is also part of a much bigger effort to regenerate the beaches along one of the world's most highly developed coasts. This includes the construction of a sea wall and an artificial reef. The project goes back to 1968, when the Dutch coastal engineering institute Delft Hydraulics was commissioned to study the erosion problems on the Gold Coast and come up with various options for 'protection of the beaches including resumption of beachfront properties'. Details of the original project proposal included, among other things:

- Providing an initial nourishment of 1.5 million cubic metres of sand to widen the beach by 30 to 50 m;
- Ongoing regular nourishment of at least 60,000 cubic metres of sand per year;
- Establishment of a permanent sand pumping pipeline to facilitate regular sand nourishment;
- Complete construction of a continuous sea wall to protect private and public beachfront assets;
- Construction of a submerged reef at Narrowneck to act as a coastal control point to stabilize the nourishment and [lastly] to improve surfing conditions.

The Tweed River bypass system resulted in the degradation of Kirra, one of the world's best waves but, at the same time, the inadvertent creation of the Superbank, which was arguably better than Kirra; but then, the sudden disappearance of the Superbank without the reappearance of Kirra. This is perhaps a hint to us that, with these kinds of schemes, fine details such as the effect on waves for surfing appear to be too difficult for us to predict. (More about this in Chapter 8.)

Undoubtedly, the best option for avoiding the effects of coastal erosion is to modify our behaviour to work around Nature instead of trying to 'stop Nature'. There are several ways we can do this. If you already have a house, hotel, walkway, road or car-park too close to the waterline, and you realize you shouldn't have put it there in the first place, you could just sit there and do nothing while the next storm comes and washes it away. The coastline will then be quickly reshaped according to the way Nature intended. In reality, people only tend to do this when the relative costs of building a sea wall or dumping millions of tonnes of sand on to the beach are considered too high, or when the coastal community is too small and unimportant to worry about.

Another option is to move the whole lot inland. A good example is the appropriately named Washaway Beach, on the Pacific Northwest coast of the USA. Here, the shoreline has retreated at an alarming 4 km in the last 75 years. So it was decided that a large coastal protection scheme would not be economically viable, and the best thing to do would be to retreat. They moved a road and a cemetery, but lost a couple of houses and a lighthouse in the process.

Lastly, and by far the most sensible option, is a proper coastal zone management scheme that stops people building their houses on coasts that are likely to erode, and stops people doing things to the natural environment that are likely to exacerbate the problem of coastal erosion. This will only work in a society where those who have the power to enforce the rules are interested in long-term benefits for everyone, and not just short-term benefits for the privileged. In other words, it is a political issue. Also, it only works properly for coastlines that are, as yet, unexploited. For those areas vulnerable to severe coastal erosion but already containing people and houses, where it's too late for prevention, then cure is the only option. Some areas have, in theory, had restrictions put on them so that things don't get any worse. The world-class rivermouth wave of Mundaka (see Chapter 3) lies inside Urdaibai, an area declared a 'biosphere reserve' by UNESCO in 1984. Some local politicians insist that, since Urdaibai is not a 'nature reserve' but a 'biosphere reserve' they are still allowed to build things on the coast.

I have already mentioned that some 'coastal protection' schemes are an attempt to rectify the unforeseen consequences of something put there previously that is now exacerbating coastal erosion. In other words, they wouldn't need to be built if someone hadn't already interfered with the coast in the first place. Bar Beach, Lagos, Nigeria, has been described as a 'textbook example' of a beach that is being eroded away because a nearby breakwater has virtually cut off the alongshore sediment supply to that beach. The breakwater was built in the early twentieth century, when we knew even less than we do now about this sort of thing. After many failed attempts to solve this problem, in 2002 engineers proposed installing a series of groynes together with a heavy sand renourishment scheme, to knock it on the head for good. The case of Bar Beach is a little different, however. The local authorities really are hoping that the latest project will stabilize the beach and the erosion will go away for good, because there are plans to make it into a gigantic new tourism complex called the Bar Beach Waterfront and Tourism Gateway Project. It will contain 'entertainment, leisure, retail, restaurant, office and residential facilities'. As I write this in 2008, there have already been several hiccups in the first stages of the project, with shops and stalls being severely inundated as a result.

At the beginning of this chapter I mentioned a beaver called John. Without doubt, if John could suddenly build a dam as big as the Aswan, then he would. He wouldn't care if there were other beavers living on the coast who might get their hotels washed away, and he wouldn't care if he was ruining the environment for future generations of beavers. But if, one day, beavers become intelligent enough to build huge dams, then they might also be intelligent enough to realize that upsetting Nature in a big way is not clever.

In summary, beavers are excellent dam-builders, and they are very good at modifying the flow of rivers. They do not care about the environment or the lives of other beavers because they are supposedly less intelligent than humans. But, by the same token, they are not intelligent enough to invent machines and methods of modifying the flow of rivers to such an extent as to cause any serious knock-on effects; nor are they intelligent enough to modify their environment in any other way that causes long-term permanent damage to beaver society. It's a paradox, because even though we are cleverer than beavers, we end up doing stupider things. If we weren't so clever, then maybe we wouldn't be so dumb.

Working on the Tweed River Bypass System near Kirra, Australia.

8 Coastal modification and the surf

Coastal structures and man-made coastal modification schemes are everywhere. On almost every kilometre of every piece of coast occupied by mankind, some aspect of the coast has been changed by us, in order to exploit the natural environment for our own use. Don't get me wrong: many of these schemes are essential for every sector of modern society. For example, we couldn't really do without the ports and harbours, into and out of which flow commodities such as fish, cars, food, clothes, computers and practically everything else we consume. Without harbour walls and rubble-mound breakwaters to protect the ships containing the products we all depend on, our lives would be very different. But, as I pointed out in Chapter 7, not all 'coastal protection' schemes are necessary. Many cater for the more affluent sectors of society, who perhaps want a nice harbour to put their expensive yachts in, or maybe a sea wall to stop the waves damaging their expensive beachside real estate. Or perhaps a series of groynes or a sand-pumping system to increase the number of square metres of beach and, therefore, the number of tourist dollars spent each year in their expensive hotels and bars.

Coastal modification has been going on for a long time – at least as long as we have had seagoing craft large enough to need some sort of port or mooring device. It was probably during the age of exploration, and then during the industrial revolution, that we really started hacking away at the coast. Doubtless many early structures were washed away almost immediately, while others, several hundred years old, remain in place today. What is certain is that, in those days, our knowledge of coastal morphodynamics must have been practically zero (and it's still pretty small nowadays, despite what coastal engineers might tell you). Back then, ports and other structures were built with virtually no consideration for the future consequences of the adjacent coastline. Nowadays, we are beginning to realize that interfering with the coastline will almost always result in some totally unpredictable side effect. We are starting to make guesses as to what these effects will be, and whether or not they will outweigh the positive effects produced by the scheme. We are still not making a very good job of this, but at least we're trying.

Since most ports, breakwaters or beach-widening projects are made to 'hold back' the waves, they must, by definition, have some effect on the waves themselves. From a surfing point of view, if you're lucky, they might create a surfing wave that wasn't there before, or improve an existing wave. Equally, they might degrade an existing surfing wave, or even totally destroy some classic surf spot.

Effects of typical man-made structures on the surf

The waves we surf are affected in various different ways by typical coastal modification

Making the most of a good wave while it lasts.

schemes, including those designed to protect people's properties from coastal erosion, as mentioned in Chapter 7. Before I get into specific cases from around the world, here are a few generic examples:

Sea walls, harbour walls or large breakwaters: Sometimes, the surfing consequences of harbour walls can be positive. You might find a wave approaching the beach at some oblique angle and then being reflected off the wall, resulting in a classic A-frame wedge as the reflection of the first wave interferes with the incoming second wave (see diagram on page 102). However, wave reflection from a breakwater can also cause serious interference to a previously smooth, backwash-free wave. Also, large structures like this never fail to alter the sediment-transport regime, with unpredictable results at beaches either side of the structure. If there was a good beachbreak or sand-covered reef there, then the change in sediment transport produced by the wall would probably have a negative effect rather than a positive one. A large breakwater might stop the waves reaching a good surfing beach inside the breakwater itself. This beach would then only break on the hugest of swells. Lastly, if the sea wall or breakwater was built right in the middle of a world-class wave, then, of course, the wave would be instantly destroyed.

Groynes: Sometimes, the accumulation of sand that occurs on the upstream side of each groyne might be advantageous as far as surfing is concerned. This sand is trapped there due to the alongshore sediment transport produced by alongshore currents, which rely on the wave approach angle being oblique to the shore. If the wave direction suddenly changed to straight-on-to-the-shore (called *shore-normal*), then a series of peeling rights or lefts might appear along the edges of these unnaturally formed sandbars, as in the diagram on page 103. These waves tend to last only a very short time, because either the swell direction switches back to its predominant oblique approach, or, if it continues in a shore-normal direction, the sandbars quickly take on a different shape. One disadvantage of having groynes in a particular area is that some beachbreak downstream of that area might end up being starved of sediment, which could mean the degradation of a perfectly good existing surf break. In this case, the new waves artificially produced by the groynes would probably never compensate for the loss of an existing natural break.

A sand renourishment scheme: Although simply moving sand from one place to another might seem very simple, the knock-on effects are often far-reaching and unpredictable. Positive effects on surfing can be the totally inadvertent generation of a world-class wave, such as the Superbank in Australia. This is extremely rare. What might happen instead is that a good wave is produced at the expense of another one. If the conditions change, and the newly created wave disappears, there is no guarantee that the original wave will return. Once we have thrown the system out of equilibrium, it may be impossible to bring it back again. Another thing that sometimes happens is that, if sand is added artificially to widen an existing beach, a good high-tide bank might disappear because the high-tide part of the beach suddenly becomes very steep due to the extra sand having been put there. A wave that was previously surfable might now just be something that surges up and down the shore without even breaking. If the grain-size characteristics of the new sand (not just the average size of the grains, but the relative distribution of all the different sizes)

(1) First incoming wave hits wall.

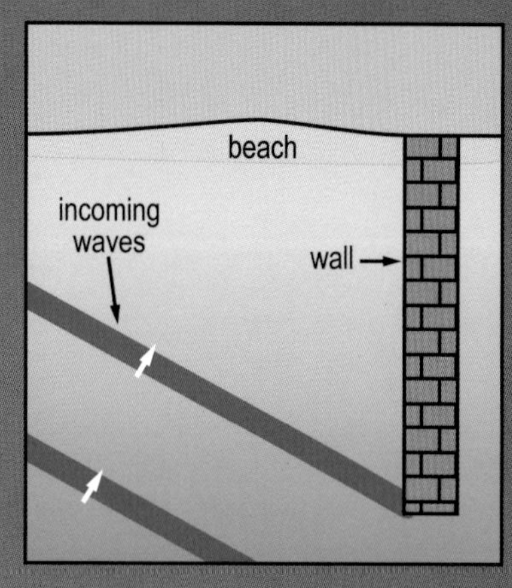

(2) First wave is reflected.

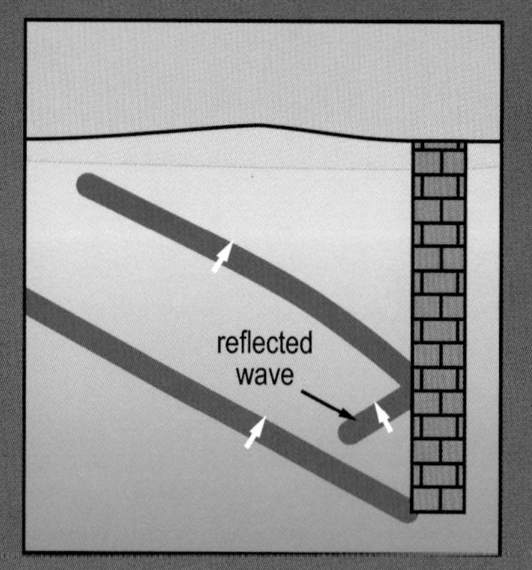

(3) Reflected wave interferes with second incoming wave, producing wedge.

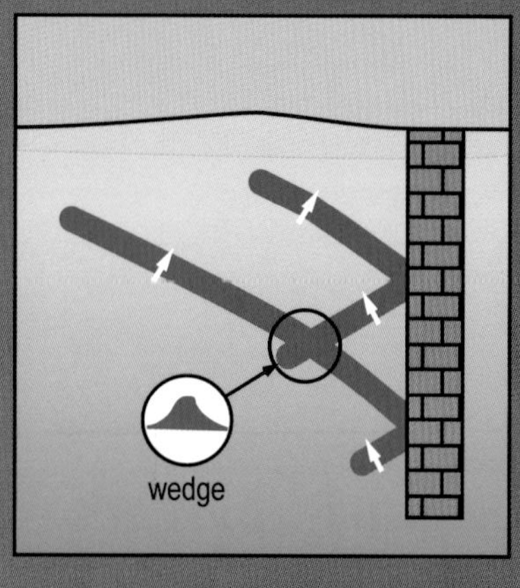

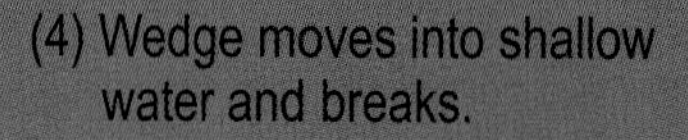

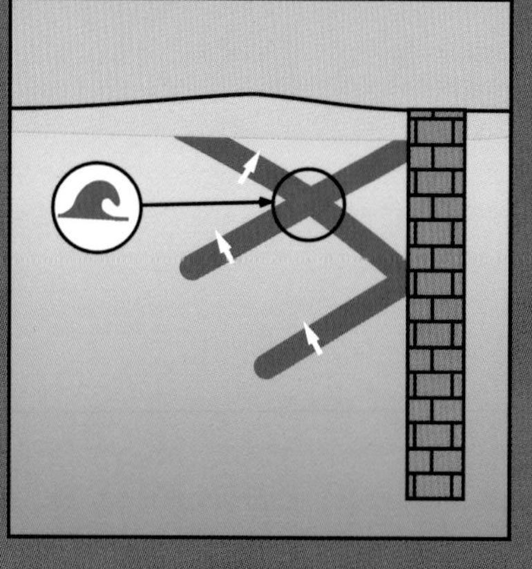

Sequence of events as a two-wave set hits a harbour wall at an oblique angle. The first reflected wave interacts with the second incoming wave to produce a wedge. The wedge propagates shoreward into shallower water and breaks. White arrows show the wave direction.

(1) Oblique wave approach: sand builds up on upstream side of groynes.

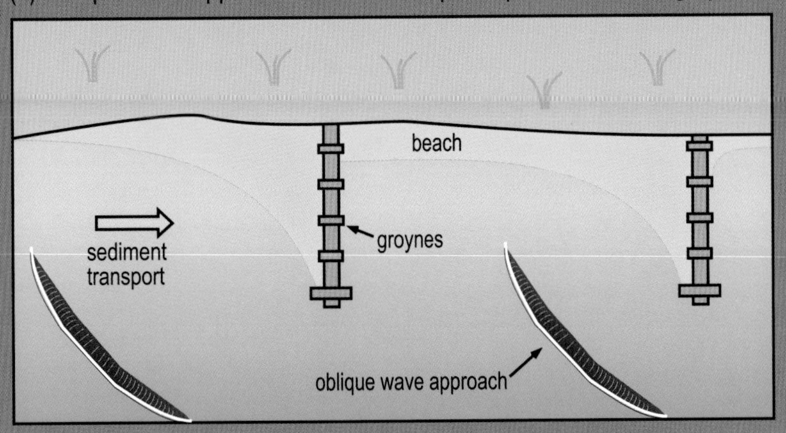

(2) Shore-normal wave approach: peeling waves at each groyne.

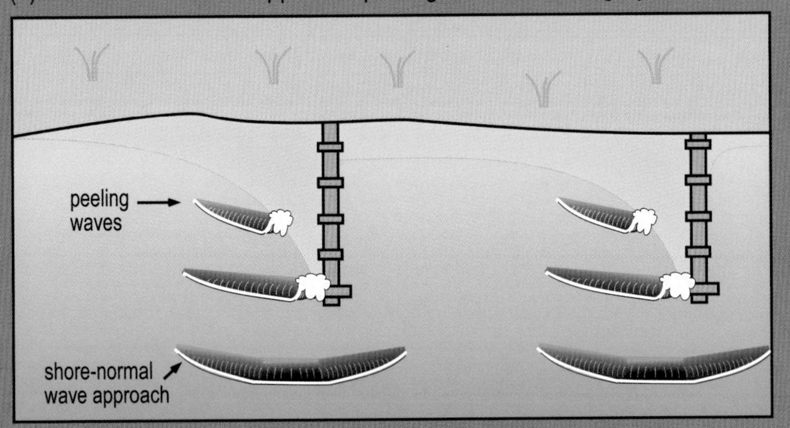

On a beach containing groynes where the swell direction is typically at an oblique angle, sand will build up on the upstream side of each groyne. If the swell direction suddenly changes to perpendicular to the coast, the waves will peel along the sandbars formed at each groyne.

are different, this can change the beach topography in unpredictable ways.

The dredging of a rivermouth: Sometimes, shipping companies and port authorities decide that the water is not deep enough for them to get their boats into and out of some rivermouth. Because rivermouths have a natural tendency to accumulate sediment, these people have an ongoing need to fight against Nature by dredging the rivermouth. Removing millions of tonnes of sand from an estuary containing a good surfing wave, where the quality of the wave itself depends directly on the sedimentology of the estuary, will obviously affect the wave. If the wave is already world-class (like Mundaka), then it is bound to make it worse. (More about this in Chapter 3.)

The past

Don't forget, some coastal structures may have been built decades or even centuries before anybody started surfing there. If that spot now happens to have a good surfing wave due to the presence of the structure, we rarely get to know what it was like before. Portreath harbour wall, Cornwall, England, was built around 1713. The wave that breaks there, known as 'The Pier', exists because the obliquely arriving swell lines wedge up against the pier and then break on a shallow reef upon which the pier was built. Before 1713 there wouldn't have been a surfable wave there at all.

The Landes area in France is a curious example. Nowadays, the coast of Les Landes is famous for some of the best beachbreaks on the planet. Behind it is the largest pine forest in Europe. Before the end of the eighteenth century, however, Les Landes was a bleak wasteland of shifting dunes and never-ending swamps. Due to the highly unstable nature of the coastal

This wave at Portreath, Cornwall, England, breaks next to a man-made pier built in 1713.

sediment, the waves might not have been as good as they are now. Instead of the tight, crisp sandbars we have nowadays, there might have been large sections of coastline with outer banks, making the waves back off and re-form endless times. In 1784, Napoleon appointed his famous engineer, Nicolas Bremontier, to stabilize the dunes. This was achieved by planting vegetation on the dunes, starting from the coast and working inland, eventually planting the entire forest we see today. Interestingly, after the success of his initial trials, Bremontier proclaimed to the authorities in Bordeaux that he had 'controlled nature'.

Of course, at some spots, things may have been the other way round. Some structures, built hundreds of years ago, may have destroyed a good surfing wave that nobody ever knew about. Rumour has it, for example, that before the building of the port of Bilbao, Spain, about two centuries ago, a series of Mundaka-like lefthanders reeled off between the now heavily industrialized towns of Zierbana and Santurtzi.

Speaking of Mundaka, around the early 1970s, a project was proposed in which almost the entire estuary would be blocked apart from a narrow channel; and a huge breakwater would be built exactly where the wave is, instantly destroying one of the world's best rivermouth waves (see diagram on page 105). What would have happened if that project had gone ahead? Well, in the early 1970s, not many people around

This is what they were going to do to Mundaka in 1972. The large breakwater sticking out on the right-hand side of the picture would have cut straight through the middle of the peak. (Note that Mundaka is spelt 'Mundaca': in those days, it was a criminal offence to speak Basque or to use the original Basque names of places and people.)

the world knew about Mundaka, and very few had ridden it. Those who had ridden it would, on the one hand, be lucky enough to treasure a memory of an experience unique to very few people, but, on the other hand, would be bitter and angry at the Spanish authorities for allowing such sacrilege to take place. Don't forget, Spain was still under the Franco dictatorship until 1975, so any protests against this sort of thing would have been quickly squashed. Even under a non-dictatorial (or semi-dictatorial) regime, there just wouldn't have been enough surfers around to make enough noise to stop it anyway. This is what has recently happened in Madeira (see below).

The present

Nowadays, at least in some parts of the world, things are getting a bit more difficult for the people who want to build coastal modification schemes. Other people, affected in some way by these schemes, through no fault of their own, are gradually beginning to get their voices heard just a little more, in order to influence the way the schemes are built so that everyone involved ends up a little happier. This includes us, the surfers. Below are two examples of recent coastal 'protection' schemes over which surfers have had quite an important influence. These are the most well-known examples in two of the most heavily populated surfing areas in the world: Southern California and the Gold Coast of Australia.

After the severe *El Niño* winter of 1982–3, an oil terminal at El Segundo on the California coast was left with a severely eroded beach. The Chevron Corporation, which owns the terminal, was concerned it might be left unprotected from any further storms. Therefore, they dumped a few thousand tonnes of sand in front of the terminal, and then stuck out a large groyne to stop the alongshore currents washing the sand away. The local authorities allowed this project to go ahead only under certain conditions, one of which was that the subsequent effect on the waves for surfing be evaluated. Thanks to pressure from the Surfrider Foundation, Chevron was also obliged to do something about it if the surf was in any way degraded. Well, it was decided that the surf really was worse after the construction of the groyne. So the Surfrider Foundation managed to negotiate a US$300,000 cheque from Chevron in order to restore the surfing conditions. The 'surf-restoration' project would take the form of an artificial reef, called Pratte's Reef.

There is a slight irony in the Pratte's Reef case: the fact that, in the end, the reef didn't work. It now just sits there, under the water, not enhancing the surf. However, the Surfrider Foundation still considers the case a resounding success. It was one of the first occasions when a government department actually 'recognized the significance of a breaking wave as a natural resource deserving of protection'.

Meanwhile, on the Gold Coast of Queensland, Australia, they don't do things by halves. In case you haven't been there, the Gold Coast is one of the most urbanized coasts in Australia, with hotels, houses, car-parks, golf courses, and every other kind of human facility, right there on the waterline. Local authorities are struggling to stop the sea from eroding the beaches away and affecting the economy of the area. They

Kirra Point, Australia, at its best.

have massive projects on the go for this very purpose, including the Tweed River Bypass System – a huge sand re-nourishment system designed to maintain or widen the beach by pumping sand from one place to another.

The Gold Coast has a history of coastal manipulation, which has affected almost all of its surf breaks in one way or another in recent years. A brief examination of the history of the area shows a constant pushing and shoving between parties of different interests, interspersed with random and unpredictable improvements and degradations to each of the various surf breaks. In some cases, man-made coastal modification schemes have blatantly ruined the surf; in others, they have improved it, either permanently or temporarily. Most of the schemes that have improved the waves have done so by shear fluke, not by design. The big difference, however, is that the local authorities – those who control the coastal manipulation – seem to be aware of the effect of their schemes on the surf. Surprisingly, the local council executives seem to have started acknowledging that the Gold Coast is one of the best and most popular surfing areas in the world, albeit only from the point of view that surfing brings money into the area. Even if, at the moment, they can only see the existence of surfing in terms of its financial repercussions on local society, at least that's better than ignoring it all together. For example, a

document published as part of the Gold Coast City Council's Shoreline Management Plan states that:

> The Gold Coast of Australia is home to what many people consider the most concentrated surfing population in Australia, if not the world. The breaks of the Gold Coast are all world-renowned and attract surfers and coastal tourists from around the world. Surfing makes a significant contribution to the economy of the Gold Coast, both from high levels of local participation as well as from tourism related to surfing.

Around 2001, the sand renourishment scheme at Tweed River resulted in the sudden and unexpected appearance of the Superbank, which, while it lasted, was one of the longest and most perfect waves in the world. What people didn't focus their attention on at the time was that the same scheme had resulted in the disappearance of Kirra, a wave that had been rifling down the point years before the Tweed River Bypass System was even dreamed of. People just forgot about Kirra, since they now had the Superbank, which was even better. However, in 2006 the Superbank disappeared just as rapidly and mysteriously as it had appeared five years before. And Kirra didn't come back. Now, in 2007, thousands of surfers are up in arms about the disappearance of Kirra. They want it back, and they want the local authorities and the people who control the sand pumping to do something about it. Hopefully, by the time you read this book, they will at least have tried.

Jardim do Mar, Madeira, before the building of the wall.

First-order coastal abuse

One reason that we, the surfers, are managing to have our voices heard in California and on the Gold Coast is because of the shear number of us. At the moment, it seems our voices are still so weak that we need a huge number to be heard over the more powerful and influential voices of coastal developers – those 'baddies' who are so good at manipulating a naive general public into believing they need something when they don't. The irony is that, so far, we have only had our voices heard in places where there are so many of us that we ourselves have already degraded the waves by making them so crowded. Pristine areas of coastline with good waves and no crowds don't have a chance, especially if they are in a country where local populations of small coastal villages are easily manipulated by government officials. Here I'm just going to describe one instance, but I'm sure there are hundreds more.

Jardim do Mar, Madeira, after the wall was built.

The surfing world was, and largely still is, hardly aware of the existence of Ponta Jardim, at Jardim do Mar on the magical Atlantic island of Madeira. Before 2003, Jardim do Mar was considered by those few who rode it as one of the finest big-wave pointbreaks on the planet. In 2003, however, the local government built a large sea wall and road sticking out directly in front of the peak, which seriously degraded the surf spot. Now, unless the swell is huge, the waves don't even break at most tides, except on the lowest springs. Even then, if the swell is big enough to break, you are likely to get a serious problem with backwash. But the most significant change is that the wave is now even more dangerous. Before the wall was built, the volcanic rocks of the natural volcanic platform (the *fajã*) provided the most efficient natural wave-energy dissipater. The wave energy was literally absorbed into the gaps in the boulder reef, providing a 'buffer zone' where the broken waves progressively lost power. Getting caught inside was always going to be a scary experience, but never life-threatening. Now, the waves hit a row of concrete blocks at full force without any dissipation. At high tide, the waves don't even break until they hit the blocks, even with swells as big as 20 ft.

In Madeira, surfers are considered a tiny, tiny minority, and the politicians in charge of tourism are convinced that tourism on Madeira will never depend on surfing. With a government having more European Union subsidies than it knows what to do with, and a local population isolated in a tiny village by huge, vertical cliffs, and easily scared by anything unfamiliar (like foreign surfers), it is no wonder we failed to stop the wall being built.

The case of Jardim do Mar is a sad one, not just because a world-class wave has been ruined, but in another very important way. The people responsible have hacked into a section of entirely natural coastline. Before, there was no man-made scheme there. Nothing whatsoever has changed to suddenly make it necessary to build a huge concrete wall in front of the village and in the middle of the surf break. How could the village suddenly need protecting? Waves of all sizes have been dissipated by the outer part of the *fajã* for thousands of years. Now they've put that wall there (see photo on page 109), they have thrown the natural system out of balance – from now on, the people of the village will have to deal with problems of coastal erosion and coastal instability for the first time. Jardim do Mar is a prime example of *first-order coastal abuse*.

Will the real shark please stand up?

The next example shows how a solid, physical, coastal modification scheme can have an effect on our surfing (not necessarily our waves) in the most unpredictable fashion. It has led directly to the loss of at least ten lives, and has stopped thousands of surfers going into the water. It shows that our image of the shark as a ruthless, unscrupulous murderer is sometimes more appropriate for some members of our own species.

From 1992 to 1999, thirty-two shark attacks occurred on the beaches of Recife, in the province of Pernambuco, North Brazil. Twenty-four of the victims were surfers. The attacks – ten of which were fatal – occurred over a meagre 20 km of coastline. The International Shark Attack File had only registered four attacks in the area between 1931 and 1992. Obviously something must have changed since 1992 to cause such an abrupt increase.

Shark experts from Pernambuco University set up a special project to work out why these attacks had occurred. The most surprising discovery they made was a close, almost uncanny, correlation between the number of attacks and the amount of boat traffic visiting the newly built port of Suape, just to the south. The super-port of Suape opened in 1990, at a cost of about US$2,000 million. According to local authorities it is 'the most complete site for the location of industrial and shipping businesses in the north-west of Brazil'. What it doesn't say in the advert is that, to build the port, they had to demolish thousands of square kilometres of mangrove and divert the course of two rivers. But even that wasn't the biggest problem.

Gradually, the Pernambuco University team began to piece together a picture.

The shark attacks seemed to be related, through a bizarre chain of events, to the existence and daily function of the port of Suape. First, the fishing boats that entered the port day and night were found to be constantly followed by a pack of hungry tiger sharks. Sharks have been known to follow the waste-laden trail of fishing boats for hundreds of kilometres. So extra boat traffic in and out of the port meant extra sharks. The construction of the port, and the massive coastal alteration that came with it, resulted in a switch in the predominant direction of the current that flows along the shore. The current tends to run along a deep channel between the shore and a shallow sandbar about a kilometre out. But now, instead of flowing from north to south, it was running from south to north – from Suape towards Recife, where there are hundreds of surfers. As a result, the sharks were being carried, by the current, straight into the line-up on the beaches of Recife. Of course, the sharks were delighted to have been conveniently steered from one yummy feast of fish offal to another of floundering, turtle-like creatures.

Meanwhile, local authorities had already found the perfect way to make the problem go away: ban surfing. Under a law passed in 1999, surfing was made illegal along a stretch of coast between Suape and Recife. The 10,000–15,000 surfers in the area had either to break the law or choose to surf outside the area. Many of the poorer ones were forced to give up all together.

The future

Even though there are many places where the effect of a man-made structure on the waves has been positive for surfing, there are probably a lot more places where the effect has been negative. This is because, out of all the millions of possible combinations of factors that influence the coastal morphology, only a few of those combinations are the right ones for producing surfable waves. The vast majority of combinations tend to produce rubbish. It follows that, if we interfere with the coast in a severe enough way a large enough number of times in enough places, the number of good waves made worse will vastly outnumber the bad ones made better. And the number of waves destroyed will vastly outnumber those produced out of the blue. So we must be careful.

One possible way to alleviate the negative effects of man-made coastal modification schemes on the surf is to replace the proposed scheme with an artificial reef; or, perhaps, to build an artificial reef to 'mitigate' the destruction of a nearby surf spot. Here we must also be very careful, especially regarding the second idea. The problem is this: the 'baddies' might latch on to the idea that they can build any concrete structure through the middle of any world-class wave, and it doesn't matter if the wave gets ruined, because we can always build an artificial reef to 'mitigate' it. If we make people believe we can create really good surfing waves using artificial reefs, it will leave the field wide open to 'coastal abusers' to destroy as many of the world's best surfing waves as they want – because for each wave destroyed we can simply create another one just down the coast.

Bearing this in mind, imagine some version of a future world in which a large proportion of the world's coastline consists of man-made structures. A great number of the surfing breaks would be artificial reefs, which, at the same time, would act as submerged breakwaters protecting tourist-covered artificial beaches from being eroded. Everything would be under control; coastal erosion would be a thing of the past, and there would no longer be any conflict of interest between coastal developers and surfers. The surfers would have their waves; tourists would have their nice sandy beaches, and the world would be a better place. Or would it?

9 Oil spills and ecocide

In this chapter I'm going to talk about what is perhaps the most blatant way in which we make the coastal environment more uncomfortable for ourselves to live in. This is the addition of toxic substances, or pollutants, into the water by us – a direct and immediately measurable way of contaminating our own environment. These substances include sewage, lead, mercury, zinc, pesticides, fertilizers, plastics, and hydrocarbons. Here I'm going to pay special attention to the last one on the list: hydrocarbons – in other words, oil. The distribution of crude oil and other oil-derived substances on to the coast, by irresponsible people who allow it to escape from their ships, is the worst form of coastal localized pollution.

Some of the people worst affected by this sort of thing are us, the surfers. Throughout the year, we spend far more time on the shoreline and in the water than anyone else. Any kind of contamination makes surfing not only unpleasant, but also dangerous. In the case of large oil spills like the ones we will look at here, surfing is totally impossible.

Of course, at the moment, without oil, we wouldn't be able to drive our cars, heat and light our homes, or take a surf trip overseas: even surfers need oil. And that oil needs to be transported from one side of the world to the other. But that doesn't give us any excuse for transporting that oil in haphazard ways, and then not making the right efforts to stop it spreading all over the coastline.

First, we'll look at two tragedies at opposite ends of the time-scale: the *Torrey Canyon*, which hit the Seven Stones reef, Cornwall, England, in March 1967; and the *Prestige*, which put thousands of tonnes of oil on the beaches of Galicia and the rest of the Spanish, French and Portuguese Atlantic coasts in December 2002. Then we'll look at a couple of studies into the way the oil has affected the ecosystems in the cases of the *Prestige* and the *Exxon Valdez*, the latter of which ran aground in Prince William Sound, Alaska, USA, in 1989.

The *Torrey Canyon*, March 1967

To most English surfers, the Seven Stones is a wave-measuring device somewhere off the coast of Cornwall that tells them whether or not there is any surf. In actual fact, the Seven Stones is a shallow reef lying between the Isles of Scilly and Land's End – one of many hazards along this treacherous coast, to be avoided by shipping at all costs. The shoreline around West Penwith, of which Land's End and the Scillies are a part, is some of the most pristine in the country. It has granite cliffs, white sand beaches, and a whole host of highly consistent, quality waves, surfed by a handful of locals who tend to keep quiet about what they've got.

The oil that leaked from the *Torrey Canyon* fouled about 150 km of Cornish beaches. Nowadays, not much evidence remains, but on certain beaches, especially if recent storm activity has caused a lot of erosion, you can still find traces of crude oil. The tiniest amount spreads itself everywhere – between your toes, on the deck of your board, in the car, the house, everywhere. And it stinks. Imagine, then, thousands of tonnes of the stuff suddenly arriving on your local beach.

Tris Coakes, a long-time surfer from Porthtowan, a few kilometres up the coast from West Penwith, remembers the day the *Torrey Canyon* oil slick arrived:

'At the time I was living within 50 m of the foreshore at Porthtowan. It was an unforgettable event that lasted for several months. I watched the first slick arrive from the top of the cliff. The waves were 3–4 ft with a west-south-west wind. As the slick moved in, the waves firstly started breaking brown and the stench of oil became more and more overwhelming. Within a couple of minutes the waves were hardly breaking as the thickness of the oil increased. An hour later the beach was up to 6 in deep in oil and remained a no-go zone for several months afterwards.'

The *Torrey Canyon* was owned by a subsidiary of Union Oil, chartered to BP, flew a Liberian flag of convenience and had an Italian crew. It was over 300 m long, took five miles to stop from cruising speed, and needed to travel half a mile just to make a 45° turn. It was an over-ambitious engineering project, commissioned by people who couldn't wait for the proper technology to become available. In short, it was an accident waiting to happen.

The *Torrey Canyon* hit the Seven Stones reef, off Land's End, England, in March 1967 ...

... and was eventually bombed to dispose of the oil and the ship.

At 08:50 hours on 18 March 1967, travelling at about 25 km per hour, the *Torrey Canyon* smashed into Pollard's Rock in the Seven Stones reef. Six of her tanks were ripped open, and thousands of tonnes of crude oil started to flood out. Soon after the impact, the leaking oil formed a massive slick which began to spread over the Celtic Sea, up the Bristol Channel and along the English Channel. The *Torrey Canyon* was the first oil spill of this scale to happen, and no plans had been made for a disaster of this type. People had no idea what to do. The detergent that was poured on the oil just made matters worse.

Dr Alan Bleakley, who had been surfing since 1964, was involved in the clean-up attempt at Newquay, the UK's premier surfing location:

'We went out in my father's boat, along with the rest of the pleasure boats in Newquay harbour. Our job was to take canisters of detergent out in the boat and deposit it on to the slicks. Far from dispersing the slicks, this created a curdled, gooey mess. The detergent offered a toxic hazard in its own right. We did go surfing that summer, although there was still a sense of lingering pollution for well over a year.'

A salvage attempt was made on the ship, but this was also a disaster. At one stage, salvage workers ended up having to jump overboard when the engine room suddenly exploded.

Meanwhile, the oil kept pumping out. Local residents, local governments and the national government were all desperate for a solution. At an emergency cabinet meeting it was decided to blow up the ship. On 28 March 1967, the matter was handed over to the military. Forty-two 2,000-kg bombs were dropped on the *Torrey Canyon*, topped off with a few thousand gallons of aviation fuel just to make sure. Unbelievably, the fire went out. More bombing raids were ordered, this time with napalm, which finally did the trick. The cliffs of Land's End were lined with mesmerized onlookers as the western sky flooded with fire.

The *Torrey Canyon* at last slipped beneath the waves on 21 April 1967. The napalm had burnt up a great deal of oil still in the ship and on the ocean, but not before thousands of tonnes had already found its way on to the beaches of Cornwall, Devon, the south coast of England, and the north coast of France.

The demise of the *Torrey Canyon* was probably triggered by a pressured captain taking a boat that was virtually impossible to steer through a very narrow channel, with no proper charts and a junior officer navigating, who happened to make a mistake. However, the ultimate responsibility surely lies with the people who decided to put such a massive, hazardous cargo in such a badly designed ship. You could almost forgive the crew – they were just following orders. And the captain, well, he was put under pressure by someone higher up. In fact, you could almost forgive those responsible for the *Torrey Canyon* disaster, and say that it was a lesson, something to avoid in the future...

The *Prestige*, November 2002

Galicia is to the Iberian Peninsula what Cornwall is to the British Isles. It is the forgotten corner, the last outpost before the Atlantic Ocean. The granite topography, the constant rain and year-round cold water give the place a harsh beauty and ensure its beaches and waves will never be overcrowded. A wide swell window and countless spots facing all directions mean that the surf is consistent and of high quality. Apart from around the more locally populated areas of Ferrol and Coruña, you might find yourself looking for someone to surf with, even in summer. Most travelling surfers prefer the easy-access, warm water and reliable weather of south-west France.

If Galicia itself is the Iberian Cornwall, then the *Costa da Morte* is the Galician version of West Penwith. This extraordinary stretch of unspoilt coastline in the far north-west, whose name means 'Coast of Death', stretches from just west of the city of Coruña to Fisterra – the Galician Land's End. It is characterized by empty, white-sand beaches, crystal-clean water, and one of the highest yearly average wave heights in the North Atlantic. The wildlife along this coast is protected under the *Red Natura 2000* scheme, and the Islas Sisargas, just off Malpica, are classified as a bird sanctuary.

Many of the people of the Costa da Morte are *percebeiros* – collectors of *percebes*, or goose barnacles, which are considered a delicacy unique to this area. These people risk their lives every day, clinging on to the rocks in all weather and wave conditions, painstakingly picking off the shellfish, one by one. About 5,000 families in this area live exclusively from the sale of shellfish they have collected themselves. The *percebeiros* are a rare example of a group of people who live in a sustainable way – where there is a very short feedback loop between over-

A clean beachbreak in a forgotten corner of north-west Spain.

collecting of *percebes* and the lack of availability of *percebes* the following season.

The Costa da Morte gives you the overall feeling that the environment in this corner of the world might just be rugged enough to protect itself. Well, unfortunately, this proved not to be the case when, in November 2002, tens of thousands of tonnes of highly poisonous fuel-oil arrived on the coast.

The 243-m-long supertanker *Prestige* was built in Japan in 1976. It was administered by a Greek company, had a Greek captain, a Philippine and Romanian crew, and was sailing under a Bahaman flag of convenience. In November 2002 it was on its way from St Petersburg, Russia, to the Straits of Gibraltar, carrying 77,000 tonnes of low-grade heavy fuel-oil. Inspections more than three years before in Holland and the USA had already detected structural fatigue in the hull. Yet the ship was still declared seaworthy by the Bahaman authorities.

The following chronology outlines what happened to the *Prestige*:

- *Wednesday 13 November 2002:* The *Prestige* springs a leak while approximately 50 km from the coast of Muxía, Costa da Morte. Oil begins to seep from two tanks. Note that this type of single-hulled vessel was designed to withstand waves of at least 12 m, and to be susceptible to damage only if found side-on to the seas with loss of steering and power. The *Prestige* was sailing under power in 5-m waves.
- *Thursday 14 November 2002:* The ship is pushed to within 10 km of the coast by strong south-westerlies. She is listing heavily, and most of the 5,000 tonnes of fuel-oil in two ruptured tanks have escaped. The crew are airlifted off the boat. Tugs are attached, the engines are restarted and, under orders from the Spanish and Galician authorities, they try to get the ship as far away from the coast as possible. Meanwhile, a huge slick is heading for the shore.

- *Tuesday 19 November 2002:* The *Prestige* finally breaks in two and sinks, letting loose a further 11,000 tonnes of oil. Nobody knows what is going to happen to the remaining 61,000 tonnes still on the ship. Scientists suspect that the hull will probably fail due to the extreme pressure of the water.
- *Around the end of November 2002:* Thousands of people from all over Europe arrive in Galicia and start trying to clean up the beaches any way they can. It seems futile – more oil arrives with every turn of the tide. Ships are sent from all over Europe to try to suck up the second slick before it arrives on the coast. The King of Spain himself visits Muxía and puts on a concerned face. Huge demonstrations are staged in the cities of Santiago de Compostela, Coruña and Pontevedra, with the motto '*Marea Negra Nunca Mais*' ('Black Tide, Never Again').
- *Friday 6 December 2002:* After systematically making its way along the whole north coast of Spain, leaving its filthy trail over Galicia, Asturias and Cantabria, the black tide finally arrives in the Basque Country. The UNESCO biosphere reserve of Urdaibai, at the entrance of which lies the world-class wave of Mundaka, is now under serious threat.
- *Mid-December 2002:* New slicks are everywhere, threatening the entire coast from Portugal to France. In Galicia, black tide number three, bigger than the last one, is on the doorstep of the original 'ground zero', Cabo Fisterra and Muxía. The *percebeiros* are deploying their own home-made barriers, tens of kilometres long, constructed from fishing net material and anything else available, including old mattresses and tin cans.
- *January to March 2003:* Surfers in France, Spain and Portugal are still unsure whether to go in the water or not. Many decide it just isn't worth it, with the unknown risk of the contamination, in addition to the cold water. Line-ups are practically empty. In France, the authorities even decide to fine those attempting to go surfing.
- *April to June 2003:* Until 2 June, all fishing is banned along Spain's Atlantic coast. Hundreds of fishing boats are converted into oil-collecting vessels, the fishermen themselves scooping up the slicks with giant spatulas. The oil is carried back to shore aboard the boats in green dustbins. This method is acknowledged as much more efficient than letting it arrive on the beaches, and then having to painstakingly clean almost every grain of sediment.
- *Summer 2003:* Summer brings home the harsh reality of the catastrophe to many who never really understood what it was all about. Suddenly, beachgoers have to try to avoid thousands of patches of oil covering the shoreline. Lifeguard stations are supplied with giant rolls of paper towels and huge drums of olive oil. Despite the toxicity of the oil, the prime concern of the authorities is to avoid an economic disaster and to keep the beaches open regardless.

So, what was the ultimate cause of the catastrophe caused by the *Prestige* oil spill? Well, similar to the *Torrey Canyon*, which was badly designed, the *Prestige* was in bad condition and should already have been scrapped. Both ships were unseaworthy vessels overloaded with dangerous cargoes and unable to do their job safely. Thirty-five years after the *Torrey Canyon*, people still get away with overloading unseaworthy vessels with dangerous cargoes. But with the *Prestige* it wasn't just that: the Spanish authorities, by making the ship head out away from the coast (away from Spanish waters) where it eventually sank, increased the radius of action of the oil

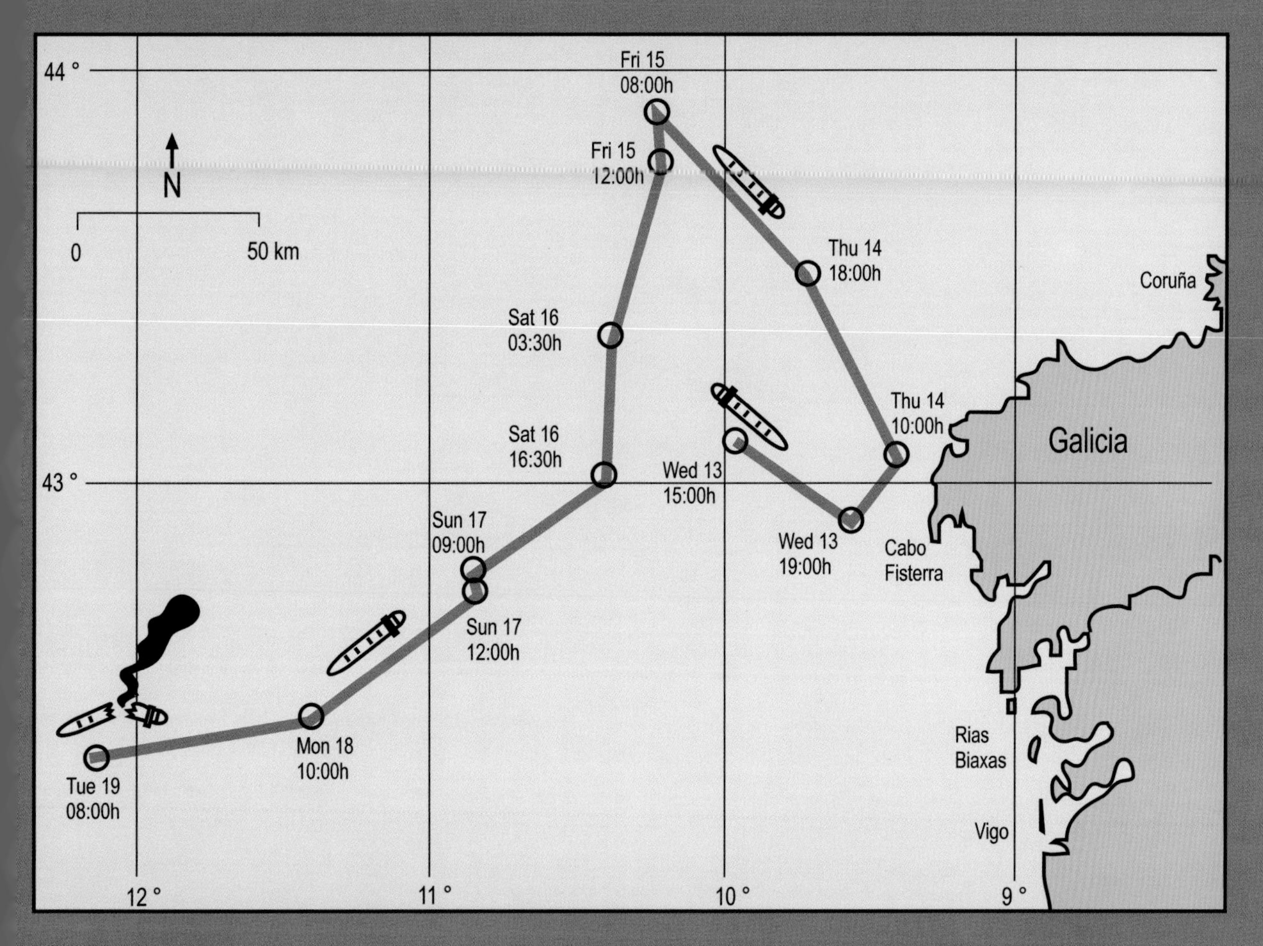

Trajectory of the *Prestige* from the moment it first started leaking oil until the final break-up and sinking six days later. All dates shown are November 2002. You can see how easy it would have been to tow the ship into a sheltered cove on the morning of Thursday 14th. This would have reduced the length of polluted coastline by a factor of thousands.

slick many hundreds of times. If the *Prestige* had been allowed to crawl into the nearest port and die there, the contamination would have been contained in a very much smaller area, as illustrated in the diagram.

At what cost?

The stories of the *Torrey Canyon* and the *Prestige* highlight many problems that don't seem to have been solved in the 35 years between the two disasters. Although the number of truly giant oil spills has gone down since the *Torrey Canyon*, something is still not right; otherwise the *Prestige* catastrophe simply would not have happened.

'Well,' you might say, 'If we want to continue driving our cars and heating our homes, we're going to have to live with the consequences, and the odd oil spill is going to be inevitable.' In other words, oil spills are part of the price we pay for our Western way of life, and unless we all go back to living in caves, then we'll just have to put up with it.

We should all reduce our oil consumption, that's obvious. But reducing our oil consumption will only go some way towards reducing the contamination of our coasts by oil spills. Obviously, if we stopped using oil all together, there would be no need to transport it anywhere, and the problem would simply go away. But if we reduced our oil consumption by, say, half, would the contamination problems caused by oil spills be reduced proportionately? Probably not, because the amount of oil we consume, and therefore the amount of oil transported, is not the only factor. More important is the way in which it is transported, and the way in which a spill is dealt with.

In the case of the *Prestige*, for example, if the ship hadn't been in such a deplorable state of repair; if its owners had taken proper responsibility, and if the authorities had done their job and not allowed it to sail, then maybe there would have been no spill at all. And once the spill had happened, if the Spanish government had acted responsibly and brought it into a port of refuge instead of trying to get it quickly out of their waters, then the contamination would have been thousands of times less widespread. And all of those issues are completely unrelated to the amount of oil being transported around the world.

The most significant ultimate cause of these events seems not to be the mere act of transporting the oil, but rather the manner in which it is transported. Then, if a spill is inevitable, the biggest factor becomes the way in which things are handled by the local authorities. Our consumption of oil *must* have a certain influence, and reducing it is something we will have to do anyway; but as long as we consume even the tiniest amount, then the highest priority ought to be to make sure it is handled in the correct way by responsible people.

Some spills have been avoided. The *New Carissa* ran aground in Oregon in 1999, but the ship's fuel was ignited to prevent it from reaching the shore.

Other significant oil spills

Since the *Torrey Canyon*, more than 50 oil spills of at least 40,000 tonnes have taken place throughout the world. Here are just a few examples – all on unspoilt areas of coastline with good surf. As you can see, apart from the *Prestige*, Galicia has had more than its fair share:

- May 1976: the *Urquiola*, containing 101,000 tonnes of crude oil hits an uncharted shoal off La Coruña, Galicia. The ship is towed offshore and explodes. About 200 km of Galician coastline are seriously contaminated, and the city of La Coruña is enveloped in a cloud of poisonous gas.
- February 1977: The *Hawaiian Patriot* catches fire and sinks about 600 km west of Honolulu, Hawaii, spilling 95,000 tonnes of crude oil and producing a slick 80 km long.
- March 1978: The *Amoco Cadiz* is wrecked off north-west France, losing 230,000 tonnes of crude oil. The result is a major environmental disaster along a 360-km stretch of unspoilt coast.
- August 1983: The *Castillo de Bellver* catches fire, breaks in two, and sinks about 100 km north of Cape Town, South Africa. Approximately 50,000 tonnes of crude oil end up in the sea, seriously affecting thousands of seabirds and mammals. A 'black rain' of airborne oil droplets falls on local wheat and sheep farms around the Cape Peninsula.
- March 1989: The *Exxon Valdez* goes aground on Bligh Reef, Prince William Sound, Alaska. As a result, 42,000 tonnes of crude oil seriously contaminate at least 2,000 km of pristine Alaskan coastline, including the Alaskan surfing area around Kodiak Island.
- December 1989: The *Khark 5* is caught in a storm and explodes off the coast of Safi, Morocco, spilling 70,000 tonnes of crude oil. The oil pollutes not only the coastline of Morocco, but also the Canary Islands.
- December 1992: The Greek tanker *Agean Sea* spills 72,000 tonnes of crude oil, and then explodes after running aground below the Torre de Hércules in La Coruña, Galicia. Three hundred kilometres of coast are saturated with oil.
- January 1993: The *Braer* runs aground and breaks up in the Shetland Islands off Northern Scotland in the most powerful Atlantic low pressure ever recorded (now called the *Braer Storm*). The entire cargo of 85,000 tonnes of crude oil is lost. Due to the conditions, the oil diffuses itself into the sediment. A considerable amount of sea life is contaminated over a wide area.

The *Amoco Cadiz* sank off north-west France in March 1978, spilling 230,000 tonnes of crude oil.

Ecotoxicology

The word 'ecotoxicology' has been defined as 'the study of toxic effects, caused by natural or synthetic pollutants, to the constituents of ecosystems; animal (including human), vegetable and microbial'. An ecotoxicological study after a major contamination event, such as an oil spill, is like a medical report after you've had a nasty accident. But, instead of saying 'Four broken ribs and a fractured collarbone; recovery time: three to six months,' it might read: 'Four extinct species, half a million dead birds and 50 human deaths due to cancer; recovery time: 15 years to never.'

The effects on the ecosystem of large oil spills might take years or even decades to develop, and it is only by studying them for many years afterwards that we can begin to understand them. Luckily, the long-term effects of the *Prestige* and other oil spills are being investigated by scientists. We will look at two such studies. The first is about the *Prestige* – the first of its kind, published three years after the event. The second, for comparison, is about the *Exxon Valdez*. Both these catastrophes happened in coastal areas of outstanding natural beauty, high productivity, and high biodiversity. It is ironic that most large oil spills seem to happen on some of the most pristine coastlines in the world. Sadly, it follows that these areas automatically become the best 'natural laboratories' for studying the long-term impact of such disasters.

The *Prestige*: first study, three years after

Just by looking at the state of the coastline after the *Prestige* spill, anyone could tell that it would take a miracle for the effects to vanish immediately, despite what the heavily censored Spanish news reports said. After a year, people were just beginning to get the first ideas about the overall impact on the ecosystem. For example, many specially protected marine reserve areas were affected by the spill and ended up having their ecosystems completely changed. *El Parque Nacional de las Islas Atlanticas*, consisting of the islands of Cies, Ons and Sálvora, is situated just off the Costa da Morte, and was devastated by the oil. About 1,000 km east, in the Basque country, the fuel had managed to cover over 70 per cent of the coastal surface area of the UNESCO biosphere reserve of Urdaibai. Urdaibai not only encompasses a whole range of unique flora and fauna, it also happens to contain Europe's most famous wave, Mundaka (see pages 41–5). One figure that was available soon after the spill was the number of dead birds. The Spanish Ornithological Society estimated a final mortality figure of between 100,000 and 250,000, representing the worst loss of its kind ever recorded in Europe. They also confirmed that, since the spill, the Common Guillemot is in grave danger of becoming extinct in Spain.

But a year after the disaster was really too early to tell what was going to happen. It took just over three years for some of the first proper results to emerge concerning the *Prestige* and its effects on the ecosystem. In 2006, biologists Rosario de la Huz and colleagues from the University of Vigo published an extensive study into the biological impacts of the spill on the coastline of Galicia. Their work focused on 17 sandy beaches, covering the entire Galician coast. They compared data on the diversity and abundance of six categories of small animals from September 1996 (before the spill) to May 2003 (after the spill). The creatures, termed macrofauna, are a good example of the type of species that can be greatly affected by a coastal contamination event, in addition to occupying a relatively low level in the food pyramid.

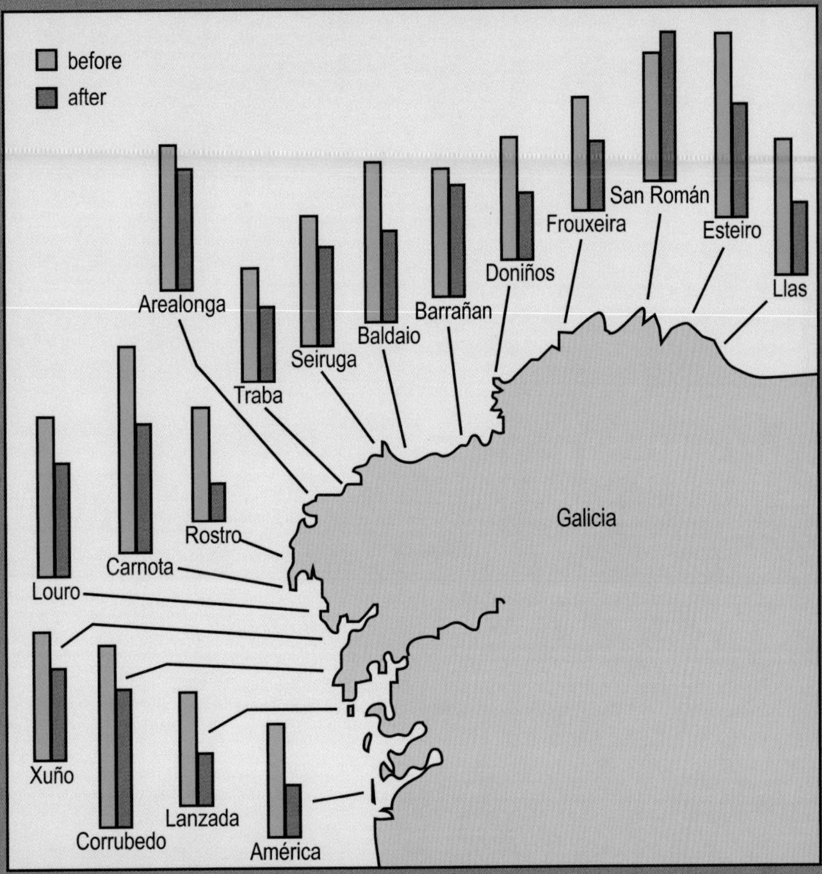

Bar plots showing proportional number of species counted by Huz and colleagues before (blue) and after (red) the *Prestige* oil spill on 17 Galician beaches. The number of species represents the biodiversity, and is vitally important for the equilibrium of the ecosystem. Every beach except San Román (third from right) shows a decrease.

During their post-spill survey in May 2003, the first thing the Huz team did was to write down their initial observations. There was a considerable amount of oil in the sediment on all the beaches studied (no surprises there). In fact, on ten of the 17 beaches the sand was not even visible beneath a thick carpet of black oil. The next thing they did was to count the number of different species present, and compare this with the data already available from September 1996. A highly significant decrease in the number of species (effectively, the biodiversity) was observed on all but one of the beaches, and, in some cases, up to two-thirds of the species had disappeared, as shown in the diagram. They then counted, for each taxonomic group, the total population of individual animals per square metre of beach area. This was also found to have decreased considerably.

Perhaps the most surprising result was that, in addition to the oil itself directly affecting the biology, the cleaning of the beaches (a secondary consequence of the oil spill) did just as much damage, if not more. This phenomenon has been noted with previous spills, such as the *Exxon Valdez* (see pages 122–3). The main reason for the damage is that vigorous cleaning of the beach removes every last trace of vegetable matter. Algal wrack (a type of seaweed), for example, is used by the macrofauna as food and shelter, particularly on the dry beach and right at the water's edge. If the macrofauna cannot live, then the larger creatures that depend on the macrofauna for food can't live either. And if they can't live, neither can the bigger ones who depend on them for food. And so on and on, up the food pyramid.

The *Exxon Valdez*: 17 years after

On 24 March 1989, the *Exxon Valdez* went aground on Bligh Reef, Prince William Sound, Alaska, spilling 42,000 tonnes of crude oil and seriously polluting over 2,000 km of unspoiled Alaskan coastline. The case of the *Exxon Valdez* is now the most highly studied example of the long-term effects of large oil spills. The extensive results of the studies on biological effects of the *Exxon Valdez*, published in the years since the spill, might be useful for seeing what lies in store for other, more recently affected coastlines, such as Galicia. By the way, if you think this is irrelevant to you because there are no surfing waves anywhere near Prince William Sound, think again. The oil reached the Kodiak Archipelago, where there are good waves and a thriving surf community

Charles Peterson and colleagues from the University of North Carolina have published a comprehensive review of all the work done on the ecotoxicological effects of the *Exxon Valdez* oil spill, from 1989 to 2006. After reviewing the vast literature available, Peterson points out that the seriousness of the event was grossly underestimated at the time. The indirect consequences (termed 'cascade' effects) were only becoming apparent all those years later. He stresses that procedures for assessing how the ecosystem will respond to traumatic contamination events, including oil tanker accidents, are still inadequate. This is mainly because such procedures do not account for some of the indirect, delayed impacts. Peterson concludes with a list of 'What we thought then' and 'What we know now' about various aspects of the spill. These are summarized as follows:

- We thought that most of the oil on most shorelines would be degraded rapidly. Now we know that it degrades at varying rates, with the oil stuck under the surface being protected from the usual effects of physical disturbance, photolysis (degradation by sunlight) and oxygenation (degradation by exposure to the air). Therefore, the oil may persist for many years. A lot of oil having been protected from the elements in this way can still be found on rocky beaches several years after a spill.
- We already knew that seabirds and marine mammals died of short-term, acute exposure, mostly due to (a) corrosion of the skin and protective coatings leading to hypothermia, and (b) ingestion of the fuel leading to direct damage to internal organs. We also had a vague idea that the poison would work its way up the food pyramid, eventually reaching the top-level predators, including ourselves. However, that was still a bit naive. We now know that the health of the animals themselves, not just whether they live or die, can affect the 'health' of the entire ecosystem. For example, in a contaminated environment, the bringing up of the young is seriously hindered, particularly in socially organized animals. This then affects the whole species, which, in turn, affects other species above and below it in the food pyramid.
- We thought the impacts on the coastline, including the ecosystem, were exclusively associated with the presence of the oil itself, directly poisoning or physically encumbering most forms of life. Now we know that the frantic cleaning of the beaches after an oil spill can cause just as much, if not more damage. Moreover, repeated clean-up operations tend to set back any ecosystem recovery already under

Do aggressive oil clean-up methods like this really do any good in the long term?

way. This is a surprising result, and quite difficult to believe. It means that having clean, sandy beaches for the tourists to lie on, or for us surfers to walk across, after a spill, might come at the price of causing even more damage to the ecosystem. Would it be better to just leave the oil there?

The importance of the health, not just the mere existence, of the affected species is worth thinking about. This is particularly true for those socially organized species such as dolphins and sea otters. It turns out that their health, or correct functioning, is important to the whole ecosystem, and therefore important to the top-level occupants (including us). In fact, a major coastal contamination event like the *Prestige* might appear to the dolphins or sea otters to be as horrific as, say, Chernobyl or Bhopal was to those poor people affected by those disasters. These were events where people didn't just die, but where entire societies – and more that just one generation – now have to live with cancers and other nasty diseases. There is one subtle difference: the creatures responsible for Chernobyl and Bhopal, and those affected by them, are members of the same species.

Ecocide

Studies into the *Exxon Valdez* and the *Prestige* oil spills are beginning to show that, by abusing the environment in this way, we are slowly but relentlessly weakening the biodiversity of the planet. The term 'ecocide' is now commonly being used to describe our gradual extermination of the planet's species and, as a result, the eventual depletion of our own resource base. Many modern scientists and philosophers, including the brilliant Jared Diamond (author of the award-winning *Guns, Germs and Steel*), suggest that ecocide has now become a more realistic threat to human society than, say, nuclear war.

The degradation and extermination of other species by ourselves – or, indeed, the degradation of any other part of nature that supports us – is environmental self-destruction on a grand scale. To get the message across, some scientists have used the anthropocentric idea that we are the most developed (intelligent?) species on the planet and, therefore, the ones upon whose shoulders the responsibility squarely falls. The planet is 'our' garden; so, if we abuse it and end up making things worse for ourselves, we have only ourselves to blame. That point of view, although useful, is a little dangerous, since it suggests that all creatures below us in the food pyramid exist only to be eaten by us. It also suggests that the climate and the landscape, so comfortable for us to live in, exist only to support us.

A more accurate view, although slightly less easy to grasp, is the one pioneered by the English scientist and philosopher James Lovelock: the Gaia principle. It is basically this: all the elements included within the living organisms of the planet and their natural environment move in harmony with each other and are self-regulating; any changes to one will be followed by adaptations of the others. For example, we humans have slowly changed throughout history to adapt to the changing environment (including other living organisms); but, at the same time, by merely existing we have subtly changed the environment itself. Now, something has happened to us, and we suddenly have the power to catastrophically change our environment over an extremely short length of time, which is throwing the whole system out of balance. If we aren't careful, that same environment will suddenly no longer support us.

Manfred, human victim of the black tide

In addition to the many hundreds of thousands of birds and mammals that have needlessly died from the black tide of the *Prestige*, there has also been a human victim. Most people agree that Manfred Gnadinter died as a direct result of the *Prestige*, murdered by those responsible for the disaster.

He was called Manfred Gnadinter, but was known simply as 'Man' or *El Alemán* (the German). He arrived in Camelle, on the Costa da Morte, one day in 1962, from Dresden, Germany. Nobody was sure why he came. They knew he was a well-educated gentleman, polite and courteous, but they knew little more. Many believe he came to Galicia disillusioned with the Western world. Perhaps he had been a businessman, or involved in Cold-War espionage. In any case, he had opted for a different kind of life. Man spent the next 40 years living alone in a small hut on the beach of Camelle, just a few metres from the raging Atlantic Ocean.

Man lived a simple life: no car, television or mortgage, no telephone, no stress. He created an open-air art gallery, full of stone sculptures reminiscent of, perhaps, Gaudí. The gallery was his pride and joy, his very livelihood. The small income he needed to survive was drawn from the one euro each tourist was asked for the privilege of browsing his works of art. He was a kind, gentle person who caused no hassle to anybody. He wanted little out of life except to be allowed to continue with his artwork. His modest lifestyle was not detrimental to his health – he could be spotted swimming great distances in the frigid Galician waters, even into his fifties.

On 18 November 2002, Manfred woke up to the stench of crude oil. His precious art gallery, yesterday a beautiful garden of multi-coloured sculptures, was now a thick mess of black tar. There was no hope of recovering it; the oil from the *Prestige* had penetrated deep into his life's work, his home and his soul. Just over a month later, Manfred was found dead. '*Morreu de melancholia*,' said the locals. He died of sadness, lost hope, a broken heart. After the black tide, he simply gave up the will to live. He may already have been sick – nobody really knows – but what is clear is that the *Prestige* finished him off.

For over 40 years Man had escaped the modern world with its gluttony and overindulgence, the world he had left behind in 1962. When, on 18 November 2002 it burst through his front door and trampled all over him, he must have thought it had been chasing him the entire time.

Many people may have thought Man primitive because he did not own a television, washing machine or bank account. However, his monk-like relinquishment of the trappings of modern society perhaps put him on a slightly higher plane than most of us. He avoided aggressiveness, territorialism and xenophobia – traits all too prevalent among so-called sophisticated people.

Some people might say that he shouldn't have built his house so close to the sea. But what about the thousands of innocent sea creatures meaninglessly destroyed – should they too have moved inland? Of course not. They lived there in harmony with their surroundings, posing no threat to themselves, each other, or those responsible for the black tide. The flow of abuse was entirely one-way.

The death of Manfred is not just another unfortunate incident to be forgotten. It is highly symbolic. Man and the Costa da Morte are the antithesis of the *Prestige* and all it stands for. The effect of the black tide on Galicia and its population – the misery imposed on so many by the greed of a few – is captured in the tragic face of Manfred.

The Planet Bites Back

In this section we look at particular aspects of the natural behaviour of our own planet, and how they can end up being disastrous for human populations, particularly those living near the coast. Most of these phenomena have existed millions of years longer than we have; but only recently, with the extreme rise in human population, have they begun to seriously affect us. In addition, through global warming, we ourselves are increasing the intensity of some of these events, and, in doing so, exacerbating their effect on us.

The first chapter in this section concerns tropical cyclones – highly intense and unpredictable storms that can cause utter destruction when they encroach upon heavily populated coastal areas, as we saw during the 2005 Atlantic Hurricane season. Tropical cyclones can also produce good surf on distant coastlines lucky enough not to be in direct path of the storm. Results from the latest studies suggest that there is definitely a link between global warming and the frequency and strength of tropical cyclones.

The second chapter is all about global warming and the effects it will have on the waves for surfing. As I am sure you know, if we don't quickly reduce our greenhouse gas emissions, we'll be looking at increased storminess, drastically rising sea levels, and more extreme rainfall patterns. Even if we are lucky enough to slow down global warming to a level that is not fatal for humankind, those things will still affect us, as surfers, much more acutely than most other people.

In the third chapter we look at tsunamis; in particular, those generated by earthquakes and by ocean island collapses. Tsunamis are not being intensified by anything we are doing, but their affect on us is becoming more noticeable as we overpopulate the coastline. A lot of research is going on into how best to detect a tsunami and then get out of the way in time, especially after the great Sumatra-Andaman Tsunami of 2004. As a surfer, you won't be surprised to hear that many of the world's best spots are located in tsunami-vulnerable areas.

10 Tropical cyclones

On 28 August 2005, while cruising through the Gulf of Mexico, Hurricane Katrina hit category 5 strength, while her minimum central pressure plummeted to around 902 mb. The next day, she went on to cause utter devastation in New Orleans and along the Mississippi coast. The final death toll from Katrina is estimated to be somewhere between 2,000 and 4,000 people; and at a cost of around a hundred thousand million dollars (US$100,000,000,000), Katrina was the most expensive 'natural disaster' ever to occur in the USA.

Three weeks later, on 19 October, Hurricane Wilma also reached category 5. Her central pressure fell from 970 mb to a staggering 882 mb in 12 hours, setting a new record for the most intense Atlantic storm ever recorded. Wilma went on to obliterate coastal properties along the coasts of Florida and on the Yucatan Peninsula.

These were just two out of an unprecedented 27 named tropical storms that occurred in the Atlantic during the 2005 hurricane season – a season that will be remembered mostly for the death and destruction brought to the Caribbean, the USA and Mexico by these storms. But it will also be remembered for an unusual number of ex-hurricanes that got swept up by the North Atlantic jet stream and re-deepened into fierce, mid-latitude depressions. These produced some amazing autumn swells for south-west-facing coasts of Europe. In some places, the surf early in the season was actually better than it was in mid-winter.

Although tropical cyclones can be a serious problem for those who live in direct path of the storms, they can also be a delight for surfers who live hundreds of kilometres away. And it doesn't look like tropical cyclones are going to go away in the near future. Indeed, some of the latest research is producing serious evidence that tropical-cyclone activity and global warming are linked.

In this chapter, we take a look at what a tropical cyclone is; how it works; how it can be our friend (by producing surf), and how it can be our enemy (by damaging coastal populations). We then look at some of the latest studies concerning the connection between global warming and tropical cyclones, and try to take a guess at what the future has in store for us.

What are tropical cyclones, and how do they work?

Tropical cyclones, like earthquakes, tsunamis, volcanoes and many other natural phenomena, are a necessary part of the functioning of the planet. They are a natural mechanism for redistributing energy in the ocean-atmosphere system. They do this by sucking up heat from the ocean surface and converting it into kinetic energy. In simple terms, the more heat that can be supplied from the sea surface, the more energy will be available to move the air molecules above it, hence the stronger the cyclone and the higher the windspeed. They are not the same as mid-latitude depressions (the storms that produce most of our surf) – they are much smaller in area, contain no warm or cold fronts, and form much nearer to the Equator.

So, how do they form? Over the tropics, the atmospheric pressure tends to be naturally low, with the warm air continually rising. But instead of rising uniformly, it does so in small chunks or 'air parcels', which tend to give rise to local thunderstorms. If there happens to be some atmospheric perturbation or anomaly – for example, if the pressure is abnormally low in one place, or there is a strong local temperature gradient – then several of these little storms might start to cluster together. This will cause a local increase in the strength of the updraft. If there is enough Coriolis force to allow the air to spiral as it rises, we have the beginnings of a tropical cyclone. (The Coriolis force is the effect of the Earth's rotation that makes fluids turn as they travel over the Earth's surface; it is zero at the Equator and increases towards the poles). The system will only continue to grow if the right combination of atmospheric and oceanic conditions exists to feed it. Among these conditions are the following:

Hurricane Katrina in the Gulf of Mexico, just before it demolished New Orleans in August 2005.

- The underlying water temperature must be above about 26°C;
- The atmosphere must have a high humidity;
- There is not much variation in the wind speed and direction as you go up through the atmosphere;
- The disturbance is far enough from the Equator for the Coriolis force to continue to have enough effect to turn the rising air into a vortex.

If the storm develops into a full-blown cyclone, it will turn into a self-perpetuating 'engine', effectively feeding itself with the heat energy of the underlying water. As the air spirals upwards, the water vapour contained within the air condenses out, releasing enormous amounts of energy. The energy released is pumped back into the

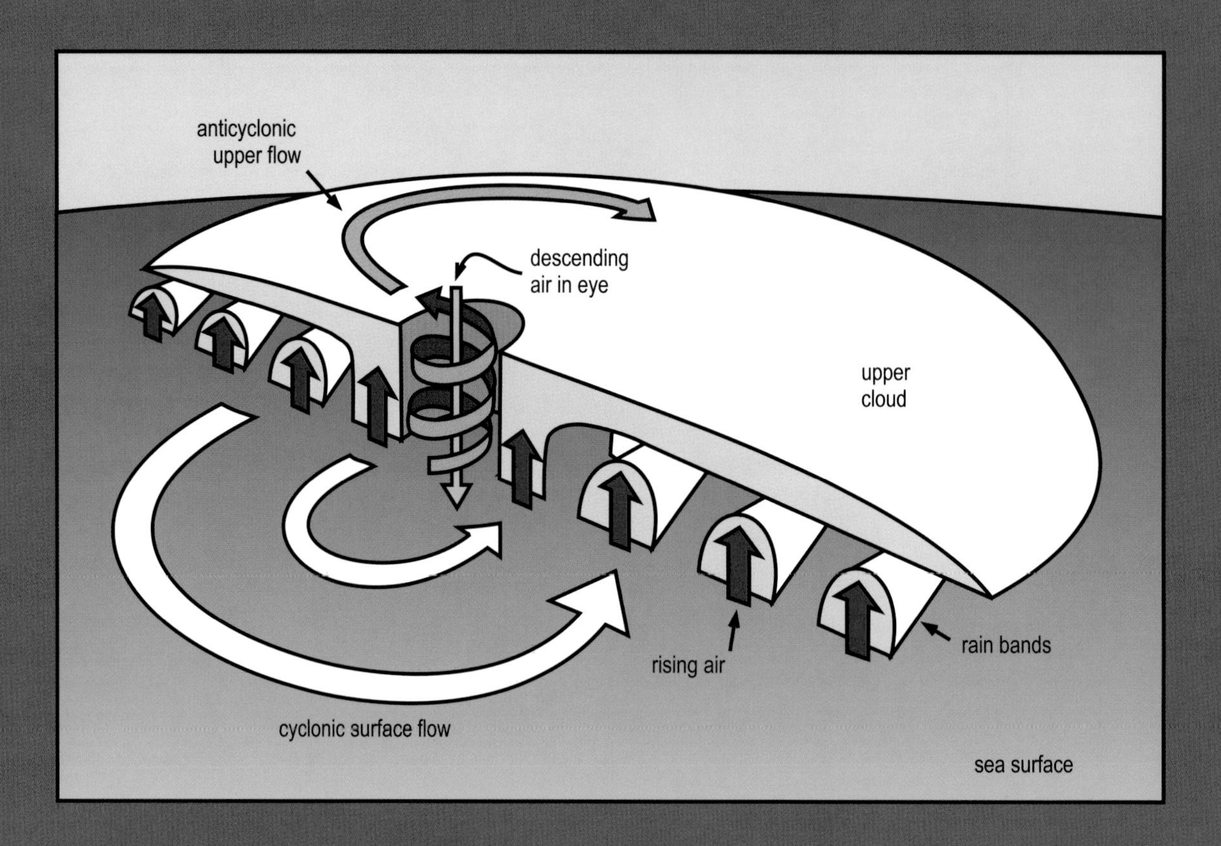

Schematic cut-away view of a fully developed tropical cyclone in the Northern hemisphere. For a system in the Southern hemisphere, the cyclonic and anticyclonic flows would be clockwise and anticlockwise respectively.

system, which maintains the updraft and sucks up yet more moist air from below. Once started, the engine will keep going as long as it remains over warm water and is able to use the warmth of that water for its fuel. Interestingly, after a tropical cyclone has passed over a particular stretch of ocean, the water temperature is noticeably cooler. The condensing water vapour is what also gives rise to those huge cumulonimbus clouds and torrential rain that come with a tropical cyclone.

Once fully established, the cyclone takes the form of a large cylindrical mass of cloud with a hole in the middle (the *eye*). Air spirals violently upwards around the outside of the eye (the *eye wall*), and there are strong cyclonic winds at the surface. Right in the centre of the eye itself, the air is actually descending, not rising. This keeps the pressure in the centre slightly higher than its surroundings, which is what creates those famous cloud-free, dry and windless conditions found in the eye. This is explained in the diagram above.

Where and when do they occur?

Throughout the world, tropical cyclones tend to form between about 5° and 30° latitude. They can't form any closer to the Equator because there wouldn't be enough Coriolis force to keep them spinning.

In the diagram below you can see the seven principal areas around the world where tropical cyclones occur. In general, the cyclone season runs from about June to November in the Northern hemisphere, and from about November to April in the Southern hemisphere. This is when the water temperature and other conditions are most favourable. In an established storm, once the sustained wind speed on the surface reaches 119 km/h, the system is then officially called a hurricane, typhoon, severe cyclonic storm, severe tropical cyclone, or just a tropical cyclone. This depends on which part of the world you are in (see map). The characteristics of the storm are not really any different from one area to another, apart from the fact that, in the Northern hemisphere they rotate anticlockwise, and in the Southern hemisphere they rotate clockwise. In the case of a typhoon, once the windspeed exceeds 241 km/h, it is then called a super-typhoon.

Tropical cyclones and surf

In addition to causing massive coastal destruction, tropical cyclones can produce excellent waves for surfing. In fact, some areas around the world rely exclusively on tropical cyclones for their surf. Cyclone swells are capable of producing some of the biggest and most powerful waves around, although these are generally less clean and shorter-lived compared with 'normal' swells from mid-latitude depressions. However, some areas, such as Queensland, Australia, do tend to receive clean, lined-up cyclone swells on a regular basis. The windspeed in a

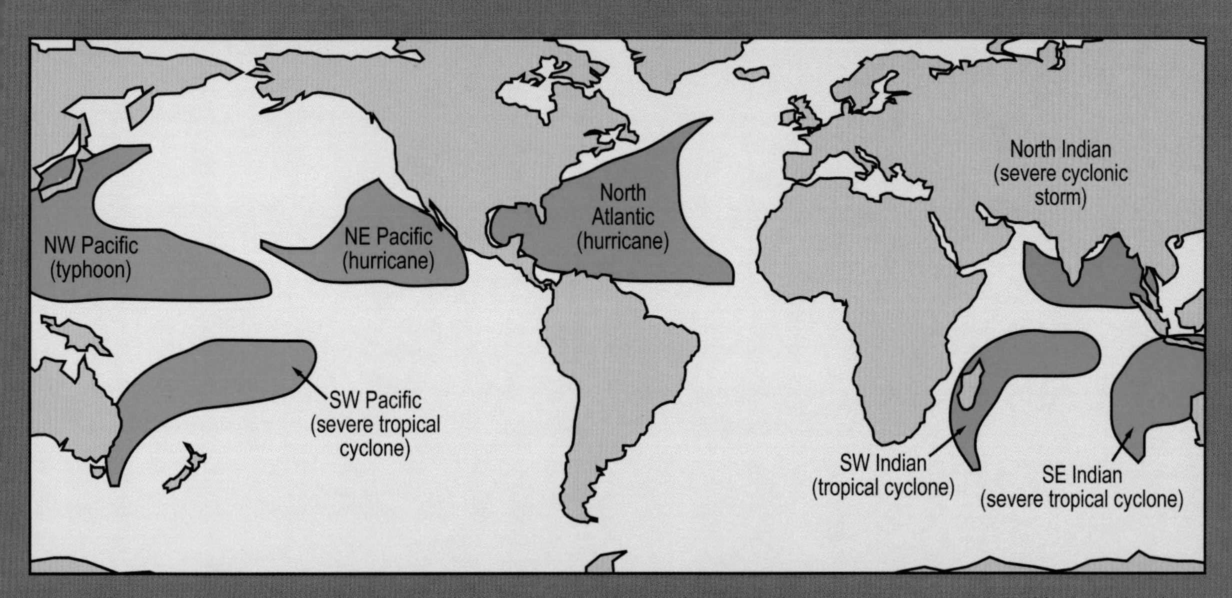

The seven principal areas (basins) where tropical cyclones are found, including the synonym used in each basin.

tropical cyclone far exceeds that in a normal mid-latitude depression, which gives it the potential to generate huge surf. In reality though, the storm moves about over the ocean so quickly that those winds rarely get a chance to blow over a decent stretch of water for long enough to create swells that are big and clean at the same time. The erratic nature of tropical cyclones means that they are notoriously difficult to predict, and so is the surf they produce. Cyclone swells can sometimes come and go in the space of a few hours. And they only occur during the actual cyclone season itself, which can vary tremendously from year to year.

Just to give a brief summary, below is a short description of where and when to expect surf in five of the main cyclone basins:

- *North-east Pacific:* Here, hurricanes spawning off the west coasts of Mexico and Central America tend to travel westwards before arcing north and then north-east. These can produce good but short-lived swells in Mexico (including Southern Baja), Central America, Southern California and Hawaii. Best season is mid-to-late summer (around July to October).
- *North-west Pacific:* The east-facing coastlines that fringe the western North Pacific, such as those of Japan, Taiwan and the Philippines, rely mainly on typhoons for their surf. These systems deepen as they track westwards towards the Philippines, and then veer north and double back into the North Pacific. They are likely to occur during late summer (June to November), and are the most frequent of all the tropical storms throughout the world.
- *South-west Indian:* Madagascar, East Africa and the east coast of South Africa occasionally receive surf from Indian Ocean cyclones forming north-west of Madagascar, before tracking west and then turning south. Best season is the Southern-hemisphere summer, between about December and March.
- *South-west Pacific:* Cyclones that form in the South Pacific and track westwards towards New Guinea and then turn south are ideal for producing classic surf in Queensland, Australia. Unlike tropical cyclones in other areas of the world, these can hang off the coast and produce surfable waves for a substantial number of days. The same cyclones can also produce surf in the north of New Zealand and on some South Pacific islands, but these swells are generally less reliable than those in Australia. Best season is around January to April.
- *North Atlantic:* Hurricanes in the North Atlantic start life as tropical disturbances around the Cape Verde Islands, and then track westwards across the ocean. They can produce good waves for a number of different regions, including the east coast of North America, the Caribbean, the eastern side of Central America, the north-east coast of South America, and the Gulf of Mexico. The best season is late summer (August to October). Hurricane activity can vary considerably year-to-year, with a known increase during *La Niña* years.

Note that, although there are not supposed to be any hurricanes in the South Atlantic, one did actually occur recently. Hurricane Catarina reached category 2 and hit the coast of southern Brazil in March 2004. This must have produced some good surf somewhere in Brazil.

Tropical cyclones in the North Atlantic and North Pacific can also produce good surf in Europe and North America respectively. After they are formed, the storms initially move westwards, being driven by the easterly trades. They then move polewards, and may eventually drift far enough from the Equator to move into latitudes containing strong westerly winds. As the storm moves towards the pole it picks up speed as it gets entrained into the westerly flow. If it still contains enough spinning motion or *vorticity*, it will quickly re-deepen as a strong and tight mid-latitude depression, or 'extra-tropical' cyclone. This phenomenon is most likely to occur at the end of summer – a transition period when the mid-latitude westerlies are just beginning to spin up in tune with the changing season, but when the water is still warm enough for any tropical cyclones to maintain their strength before they are picked up by the westerlies.

Barbados is one place that gets great surf, but is also highly susceptible to a direct hit from an Atlantic hurricane.

This 'reanimation' of tropical cyclones is particularly common in the North Atlantic. The storms spin off the Eastern Seaboard of the USA and re-deepen as they track eastwards, usually ending up just north of the Azores. The swells generated by these storms can be uncharacteristically powerful for this time of year as they hit the coasts of Europe. Because these lows track further south than normal, the best areas are those that face west or south-west. Places such as Cornwall in England, or Cadiz in south-west Spain sometimes get their biggest and cleanest waves from ex-hurricane swells. In September and October 2005, the south-west-facing coasts of Europe had more surf than the north-west-facing coasts of France, Spain and Portugal. The number of ex-hurricane swells in the autumn of 2005 was exceptional, if not beyond belief. It was, of course, linked to the excessive number of hurricanes that formed in the Atlantic in 2005 – hurricanes such as Katrina and Wilma, which caused so much death and destruction on the other side of the Atlantic.

Tropical cyclones and coastal destruction

Although tropical cyclones are a natural and necessary part of the planet's functioning, they still cause a great deal of problems for people who live near the coast. In some parts of the world, especially in developing countries like Bangladesh, massive populations have existed in low-lying coastal areas for hundreds of years. They were already there a long time before we knew anything about tropical cyclones. For these people, the sudden arrival of a severe cyclonic storm on their doorstep means catastrophe, and it really is not their fault for being there. In other parts of the world, coastal populations are growing simply because rich people want a 'better lifestyle', or because people from inland areas want to enjoy the coast for one or two weeks of the year. In this case, the people understand enough about tropical cyclones to know what the risks are; and it is up to them whether they move to the coast or not. Even so, they still keep populating the coastline, and complaining when their houses and hotels get washed away. In some areas, the rate of increase in cyclone damage to coastal properties is increasing in direct proportion to the rate of increase in coastal populations. I'll say more about that in a moment.

Even though Katrina, with around 2,000 to 4,000 deaths, was one of the most deadly tropical cyclones in history, it wasn't *the* deadliest. The fact that it hit the USA meant that it was big news. I think it is important to mention that quite a few other tropical cyclones have been a lot more serious than Katrina, but have been a lot less publicized, particularly in the developing world. Below is a brief list:

- In November 1970, the **Bhola Cyclone** made landfall on the Ganges Delta area of Bangladesh. It was a category 3 storm, with peak windspeeds of 185 km/h. The death toll was difficult to establish, but the most conservative estimate was around 300,000. Some other estimates put the figure at over 1,000,000. The Ganges Delta is by far the most susceptible part of the world to deaths from coastal flooding. It is not only one of the most densely populated parts of the planet, but the 140 million people who live there are very close to sea level (see map on page 135).
- In August 1975, **Typhoon Nina** hit the coast of Taiwan as a category-three storm. It passed over the island, across the Straits of Formosa and into China, where it caused the failing of 62 dams

and at least 100,000 deaths, not just directly from the flooding but also from an epidemic that quickly spread throughout the area.

- Tropical cyclones in the Atlantic tend to be the best documented, with the **Great Hurricane** of 1780 being the most devastating. This storm killed about 22,000 people on the islands of Martinique, St Eustatius and Barbados. The well-known **Galveston Hurricane** of 1900, which is still the most deadly hurricane to hit the USA, is estimated to have killed at least 8,000 people. More recently, **Hurricane Mitch** caused extensive flooding in Honduras and Nicaragua in October 1998, leading to approximately 11,000 deaths.

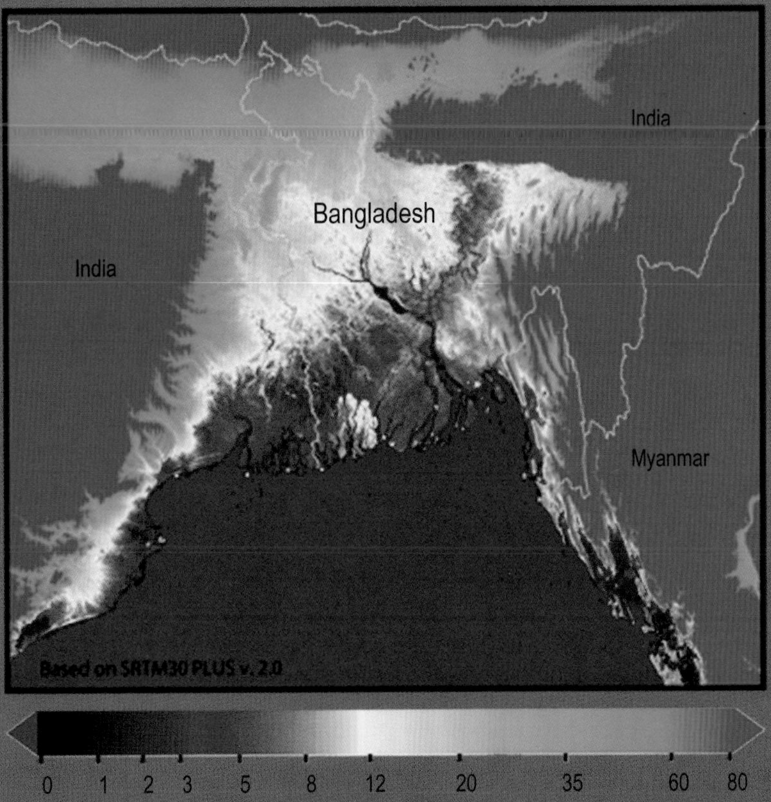

From this map you can see how low-lying most of Bangladesh is. The colour contours are height in metres above sea level.

Tropical cyclones and global warming

In recent decades, the strength of tropical cyclones has been gradually increasing. Not only are the most destructive cyclones becoming more frequent, but the total energy imparted by all tropical cyclones – their potential for destruction – is increasing. Understandably, people have been putting two and two together and suggesting that it could be something to do with global warming.

Many recently published studies have identified an unmistakable worldwide increase in tropical-cyclone activity over the last few decades, together with a notable rise in sea-surface temperature. Tropical-cyclone strength is known to respond to sea-surface temperature, and so it is logical to assume that the two are linked. The following two examples are typical of such studies, although there have been many more. Note that both articles were submitted before their authors knew anything about the unprecedented Atlantic hurricane season of 2005.

A tropical cyclone doesn't care how expensive your yacht is.

First, Kerry Emanuel, of the Massachusetts Institute of Technology, in an article in *Nature*, chose a parameter that expresses the total power dissipation of each tropical cyclone. The total value of this parameter was then calculated for all the tropical cyclones in each season over the previous 30 years. Results showed that it had increased considerably over that time. The parameter is based on the cube of the wind speed integrated over the life of each storm, which responds to both storm intensity and duration. Because it expresses the power dissipated by the cyclones – the energy imparted upon the sea or land surface – it can be thought of as a proxy for their overall destructive potential. Results showed that it had increased considerably over the 30-year period. Then, Peter Webster and colleagues from the Georgia Institute of Technology published an article in *Science*, in which they examined the total number of tropical cyclones per season in all the ocean basins over the same 30-year stretch. Unlike any previous study, however, they looked separately at the number of storms in each category on the Saffir-Simpson scale. They found a significant increase in the number of category 4 and 5 storms, but virtually

The Saffir-Simpson Scale

Tropical cyclones with windspeeds that exceed 119 km/h are categorized according to the *Saffir-Simpson Scale*, which runs from category 1 to category 5. The scale was originally designed for hurricanes in the North Atlantic, but has since been used for tropical cyclones worldwide. Precise definitions of the expected levels of damage for each Saffir-Simpson number are set out below, adapted from the National Hurricane Centre in Florida.

Category 1:

- Winds 119–153 km/h
- Damage primarily to unanchored mobile homes, shrubs and trees
- Some damage to poorly constructed signs
- Some coastal road flooding and minor pier damage

Category 2:

- Winds 154–177 km/h
- Some roofing material, door and window damage
- Considerable damage to shrubs and trees, with some trees blown down
- Considerable damage to mobile homes and piers
- Coastal and low-lying escape routes flood two to four hours before the arrival of the storm centre
- Small craft in unprotected anchorages break moorings

Category 3:

- Winds 178–209 km/h
- Some structural damage to small residences
- Large trees blown down
- Mobile homes completely destroyed
- Low-lying escape routes cut by rising water three to five hours before arrival of storm centre
- Coastal flooding destroys smaller structures
- Larger structures damaged by floating debris
- Terrain continuously lower than 1.5 m above sea level may be flooded 13 km inland; evacuation of low-lying residences within several blocks of the shoreline

Category 4:

- Winds 210–249 km/h
- Extensive wall failures and some complete roof structure failures on small residences
- All shrubs and trees blown down
- Complete destruction of mobile homes
- Extensive damage to doors and windows
- Low-lying escape routes cut by rising water three to five hours before arrival of storm centre
- Major damage to lower floors of structures near the shore
- Flooding of terrain lower than 3 m above sea level
- Massive evacuation of residential areas up to 10 km inland

Category 5:

- Winds above 249 km/h
- Complete roof failure on residences and industrial buildings
- Some complete building failures with small utility buildings blown away
- All shrubs and trees blown down
- Complete destruction of mobile homes
- Low-lying escape routes cut by rising water three to five hours before arrival of storm centre
- Major damage to lower floors of all structures located less than 5 m above sea level
- Massive evacuation of residential areas within 8–16 km of the coast

A category 5 tropical cyclone seen from space. Hurricane Felix, from the Earth-Orbiting International Space Station, 3 September 2007.

no increase in categories 1 to 3. Since the strongest cyclones are the ones that normally cause most of the damage, Webster's result suggests a worldwide increase in the destructive potential of tropical cyclones.

Since rising sea-surface temperatures are now known to be a consequence of global warming, and the strength of tropical cyclones is directly related to sea-surface temperature, it is tempting to 'close the loop' and suggest that the increase in tropical-cyclone activity is down to global warming. Before Hurricane Katrina and the extraordinary North Atlantic hurricane season of 2005, critics of these and other similar studies were quick to point out that 30 years is a very short time, and so the apparent increase could all just be part of a long-term climatic cycle such as the Atlantic Multidecadal Oscillation. Moreover, mathematical modellers who tried to simulate how tropical-cyclone activity would change by 2080 managed to come up with a 5 per cent increase, which could easily be swamped by natural variations and the effect of these cycles. For a while, the general consensus was that we might be jumping the gun by suggesting that an increase in tropical-cyclone activity has anything to do with global warming.

However, since the 2005 season, a great deal more scientific effort has gone into finding out whether or not the increase is due to global warming. Evidence has now emerged that it is probably *not* just part of a cycle after all. Simulations suggest that tropical cyclones will become significantly more frequent and more destructive in the future, and there is also more evidence that the increase in sea temperatures around hurricane-spawning grounds is linked to the emission of greenhouse gases. The following two studies, for example, seem to point to global warming as being an important factor in the recent increase in tropical-cyclone activity.

In a paper published in 2006, Kevin Trenberth and Dennis Shea examined the anomalously high sea-surface temperatures found in the tropical North Atlantic during 2005. These high temperatures are acknowledged as having been responsible for fuelling hurricanes like Katrina and Wilma. While the scientific community agreed that warmer water leads to more tropical cyclones, it was still not quite sure whether the tropical North Atlantic was warmer than usual because of global warming, or because of those decade-long natural cycles. So, Trenberth and Shea carefully examined statistical records of global sea-surface temperature going back over 100 years, and found that the Atlantic Multidecadal Oscillation accounted for only about 12 per cent of the temperature anomaly during the 2005 hurricane season, whereas global warming accounted for about 46 per cent. Meanwhile, a group of scientists from eight different research establishments, including the National Centre for Atmospheric Research, used simulations from 22 different climate models to show that temperature increases in specific hurricane-forming areas of the tropical North Atlantic and Pacific are very likely to be linked to greenhouse-gas emissions. They found that the observed sea-surface temperature rise in these areas in the last century has an 84 per cent chance of being caused by factors other than 'natural' ones. 'Unnatural' factors mean human activities – principally the emission of greenhouse gases into the atmosphere.

Lastly, if the overriding concern is the increase in the damage to coastal real estate and the lives of those who live in it, then the effect of global warming on tropical-cyclone activity can look quite different depending on where you are in the world. For example, the Gulf of Mexico, Florida, most Caribbean islands and the Yucatan Peninsula have a steadily growing population which is also becoming more affluent. Everybody wants to move to the coast, and everybody wants a nice big house. According to calculations by Roger Pielke of the University of Colorado, between now and 2050 the increase in damage caused to coastal properties directly attributable to population growth and wealth will be between 22 and 60 times more significant that the increase in damage attributable to the effects of global warming on hurricane activity. In other words, even if there is no change in hurricane activity, hurricanes will still produce more and more casualties in the coming years, simply because of the swelling coastal populations. However, now look at, say, the Ganges Delta in Bangladesh, where more than 100,000,000 people live in extreme poverty in an area regularly devastated by coastal flooding. Those people are not there because they want to have a nice hotel next to a sunny beach; they are there because they were born there and have no choice but to stay. The extreme sensitivity of this area to any phenomenon that leads to coastal flooding implies that any increase in tropical-cyclone activity, no matter how small, will have a huge effect on the existing population. And if that increase *is* due to global warming, then we, in the first world, are primarily responsible.

11 Global warming and the surf

Global warming is really happening. Even as recently as the 1990s, many scientists still didn't want to stick their necks out and admit it; but now, the overwhelming majority agree that global warming is here with us. The evidence is mounting up ever-faster, with records from tree rings, ice cores and ancient coral telling us that the planet is warmer than it has been for at least a thousand years. The majority of that warming has occurred since the industrial revolution, and the fastest temperature rise has been in the last 30 years.

Global warming is unequivocally related to human activities; in particular, the pumping of greenhouse gases into the atmosphere. Scientists working for the Intergovernmental Panel on Climate Change (IPCC) are now absolutely certain that this is true. They are also certain that global warming is continuing to accelerate, and that unpredictable runaway effects might cause previously unimaginable catastrophic events. The IPCC Fourth Assessment Report, drawn up by more than 600 scientists from 40 different countries, was published in 2007. Before being accepted, it was peer-reviewed by another 600 experts and examined by representatives from 113 governments. The most striking two statements in the report are that warming of the climate system is 'unequivocal', and that the recent increase in global temperatures is 'very likely due to our own emission of greenhouse gases into the atmosphere'. In the report, the term 'very likely' is precisely quantified to mean 'the assessed likelihood, using expert judgment, is over 90 percent'.

We surfers, who live at the interface between the land and the sea, and who depend so directly on the natural oscillations of the sea surface and the atmosphere, ought to be the first people to be concerned about this. We are highly sensitive to any changes in these natural systems, and will be some of the first to be affected by them. Most of us also live in the developed world, and are part of the very society that is causing the problem.

So, in this chapter I'm going to take a look at how global warming might affect us in the future, from a surfing point of view. I'm not going to get too political, or too technical, and I'm not going to tell you what you should be doing to reduce your own carbon emissions. I'm just going to list a few aspects of climate change that might have a direct bearing on our lives as surfers and coastal dwellers. First, though, here is a very quick recap on global warming.

Is it real, and is it our fault?

There is now enough proof to show that the overall temperature of our planet has increased considerably in the last few years. The first piece of conclusive evidence was a graph originating from two scientific papers published by Michael Mann of the University of Virginia – the first in *Nature* in 1998, and the other in *Geophysical Research Letters* in 1999. The famous plot, termed the 'hockey stick' (see the chart on page 141), showed values of the Earth's temperature over the last 1,000 years. In the plot, the temperature

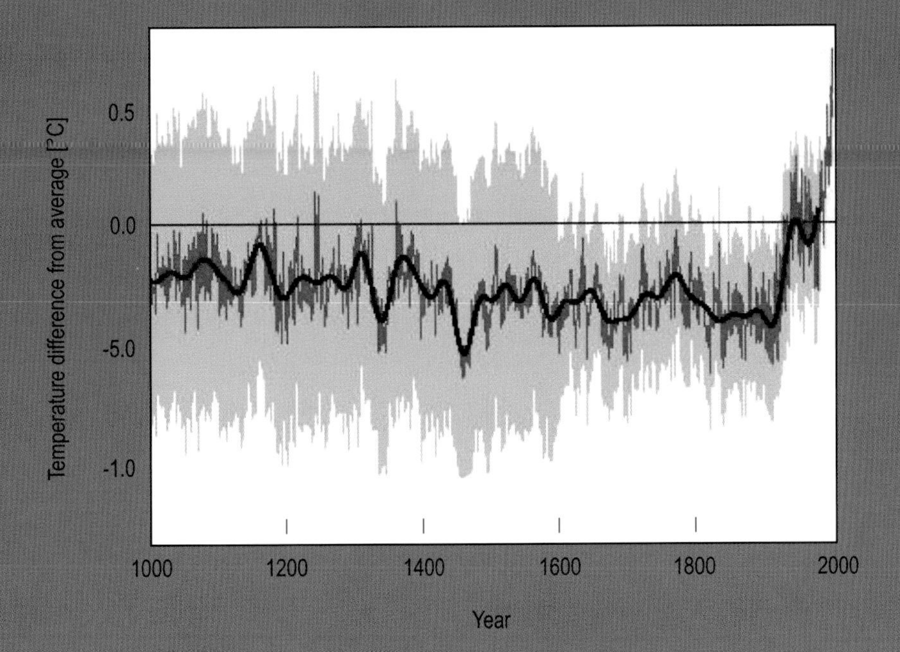

Northern hemisphere temperature anomaly relative to 1961–90 average (the famous 'hockey stick' plot). The red line shows observed temperatures, while the blue line shows temperatures inferred from proxies such as ice cores, corals and tree rings.

remains fairly constant for the most part, but then suddenly goes sky-high for the last few decades of the twentieth century. The recent data was obtained from real temperature readings going back about a century, and the more ancient data had to be inferred from 'proxies' such as tree rings and ice cores.

The 'hockey-stick' became well known because it was published in the IPCC Third Assessment Report of 2001. Not surprisingly, it was hotly contested and subject to fierce criticism. This went on for several years, mostly by people with an interest in making others believe that climate change wasn't happening. However, since it was published, literally hundreds of studies have been done to test and re-test the 'hockey stick'. Time and time again, these studies showed irrefutably that Mann was correct, and that the Earth really has become a lot warmer since the industrial revolution. The vast amount of data now available shows an average temperature rise of about 0.8°C in the Earth's atmosphere over the last century. This doesn't seem very much, but if you look at the graph, the rate of change of temperature is much sharper in the last 100 years compared with the previous 900 years. Therefore, if it carries on rising at the present rate, things could get out of control before we know it.

So, the temperature has gone up, but maybe it's all natural. When I say 'natural' I mean it might have happened anyway, even if we hadn't interfered. For example, how do we know that the changes are not due to volcanic eruptions, or perturbations in the Earth's orbit, or solar radiation anomalies, all of which have caused major climate changes at some time in the Earth's history?

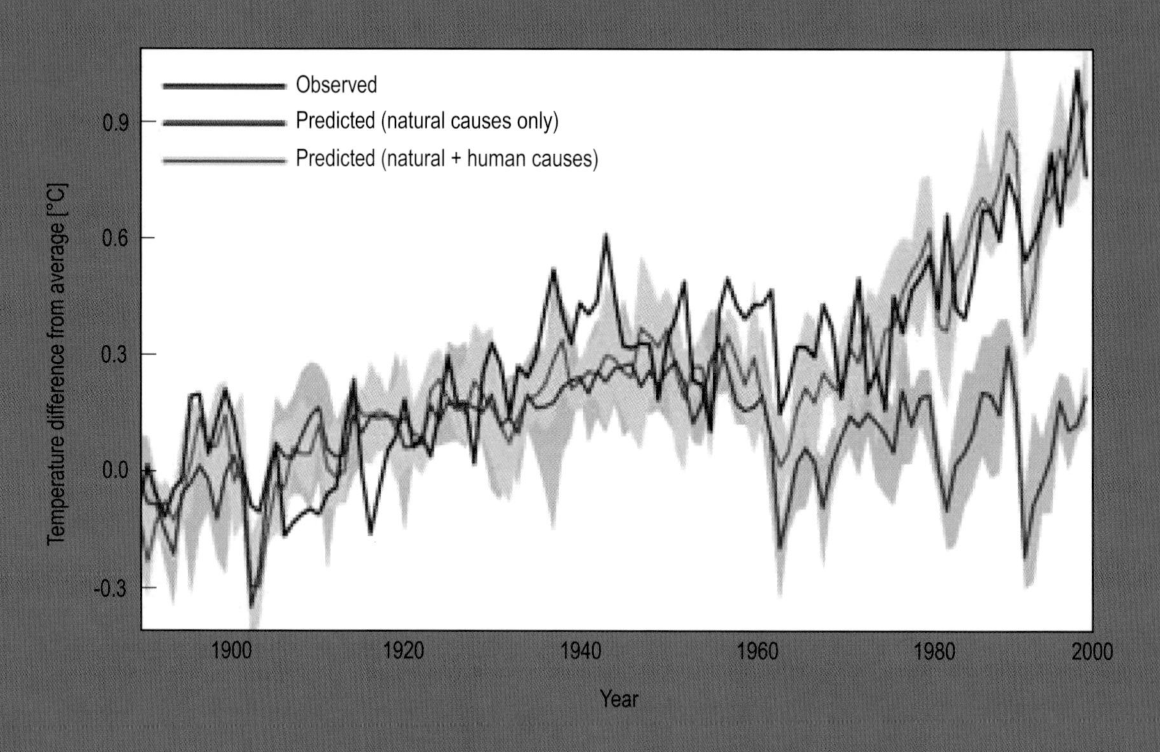

Global average temperature anomaly relative to 1890–1919 average. The black line is the observed temperature; the blue line is a simulation using only 'natural' influences on climate (volcanoes and solar variations), and the red line is a simulation that includes human influences such as greenhouse gases. The red line follows the black one, but the blue line doesn't follow the black one. This implies that the model only predicts the correct temperature variation when taking into account human influences on the climate.

People love to ask that question, because another way of phrasing it is, 'Is it our fault?', or 'Perhaps it isn't our fault.' And if it isn't our fault, then it's not our responsibility.

One of the reasons the IPCC was set up in 1988 was to address that question. Early on, the evidence already started pointing towards us as the culprits. For example, the second IPCC Assessment Report, published in 1995, stated that 'The balance of evidence suggests a discernible human influence on global climate'; and then, in the Third Report, published in 2001: 'There is new and stronger evidence that most of the warming observed over the last 50 years is attributable to human activities'. Most recently, in 2007, in the Fourth Report, they state: 'Most of the observed increase in globally averaged temperatures since the mid-20th century is *very likely* [over a 90 per cent probability] due to the observed increase in anthropogenic greenhouse gas concentrations.'

But how do they know that? Well, among hundreds of studies that give similar results, perhaps the easiest to understand is one published by the National Centre for Atmospheric Research (NCAR). Scientists at NCAR used a computer model to simulate the Earth's temperature variation over the last century or so, while switching on and off various different contributing factors. They compared this with a temperature curve that had been plotted using real measured data. The factors they switched on and off included 'natural' ones like volcanoes and solar radiation anomalies, and 'unnatural' ones such as atmospheric greenhouse-gas emissions. Only the last one, greenhouse gases, was caused by us humans. With greenhouse-gas emissions switched off, the simulated temperature change looked nothing like what really happened; principally, it did not have that sharp upward swing at the end. When they switched it back in, however, the graph looked remarkably like reality. The results therefore suggest that the sharp temperature increase over the last few decades would not have happened without our input of greenhouse gases to the atmosphere.

The greenhouse effect

Just in case you're still not convinced, I'll explain in very simple terms the relationship between our consumption of hydrocarbons, the emission of greenhouse gases into the atmosphere, and global warming. First of all, in the outer atmosphere there is a layer of so-called greenhouse gases, including carbon dioxide. This layer acts as a filter to electromagnetic radiation, blocking out some types but letting through others. To be more specific, it blocks out lower-frequency radiation such as infrared, but lets through higher-frequency radiation such as visible light and ultraviolet. Incoming sunlight contains a broad band of radiation, including a lot of high-frequency stuff which easily penetrates the greenhouse layer. The intensity of this radiation, once it reaches the Earth's surface, is more than enough to heat it up. Once the surface of the Earth is hot, it re-radiates some of that heat into the atmosphere. But, this time, it re-radiates that heat at lower frequencies, in the infrared band. When this radiation hits the greenhouse layer from below, most of it is not allowed through. Instead, it is absorbed by the greenhouse gases and re-emitted once again, in both directions, including back towards the Earth's surface. The greenhouse layer, by acting as a kind of one-way valve, traps some of the Sun's heat in the lower atmosphere.

The link between the greenhouse effect and us is as follows. In the last 150 years or so, since the industrial revolution, we have been burning hydrocarbons at vastly increasing rates. The burning of hydrocarbons directly results in the emission of extra carbon dioxide into the atmosphere. This is exacerbated even more by deforestation, which effectively removes a natural way of absorbing carbon dioxide, allowing more to end up in the atmosphere. The result is a denser greenhouse layer and a hotter Earth. If we keep pumping carbon dioxide into the atmosphere and keep cutting down trees at the present rate, the greenhouse layer is going to get thicker, not thinner. Since the industrial revolution, the concentration of carbon dioxide in the atmosphere has risen from 280 to 360 parts per million, after being fairly stable for the previous 800 years. Forecasts have shown that, if we don't do something about it, the concentration could increase to over 900 parts per million by the year 2100.

Now, on to the ways in which global warming might specifically affect our lives from a surfing point of view. Of course, in the most disastrous of cases, global warming will bring us to the brink of societal collapse and surfing will be a forgotten luxury. However, for the moment, let's assume that the effects will be relatively mild, and will allow us to continue surfing in some parts of the world at least. I'm going to describe a few of the more well-known consequences of global warming, and how each might affect our lives as surfers. They include: ocean storminess, including tropical-storm activity; water quality and pollution; glacial melting and sea-level rise, and, lastly, a bizarre effect where the shutdown of the Gulf Stream might mean freezing waters for northern Europe.

Storminess

A general heating up of the planet doesn't necessarily mean that all areas will heat up at the same rate. Due to some important physical mechanisms, there will always be disparities in temperature rise between different areas of the Earth's surface. The most important factor stems from a basic physical property called *latent heat of fusion*. This is the energy you need to pump into a substance to make it turn from a solid into a liquid (from ice to water, for example). As a simple example, imagine a block of ice and a glass of water, side by side, both being heated up by, say, a powerful infrared lamp. The water starts off warmer than the ice, and initially they both get warmer at the same rate. The temperature differential between the two should remain constant as they both receive the same amount of heat energy from the lamp. However, as soon as the ice starts to melt, its temperature stops increasing, even though it continues to receive energy. This is because the energy is being used to melt the ice instead of increase its temperature. Meanwhile, the glass of water continues to heat up. As a result the the temperature gap between the two widens.

The Equator-to-pole temperature difference is the fundamental driving force behind all our weather. The global circulation patterns in the atmosphere and ocean exist because the air and water are conducting and redistributing heat energy around the planet to maintain an overall temperature balance. The greater the temperature differential between poles and Equator, the stronger the atmospheric and oceanic circulation patterns need to be to redistribute all that heat. And stronger circulation patterns mean faster oceanic currents, faster atmospheric air streams and, basically, stormier weather. With all the glacial melting at the poles, a great deal of heat energy is being 'lost' through latent heat of fusion. As the entire planet gets warmer, the temperature rise at the poles will be smaller than the temperature rise at the Equator. And if the Equator-to-pole temperature differential gets wider, storminess is likely to increase. This is particularly true over the oceans, since the oceanic currents and the atmospheric circulation patterns are closely linked.

To quantify the 'storminess' of the atmosphere over a particular part of the world, scientists use a variety of indices – numbers designed to reflect whereabouts we are within some cyclic behavioural pattern. They are often based on atmospheric measurements such as north-south pressure differences. These numbers can also tell us whether there is any systematic increase or decrease in that storminess over long time-scales. And a systematic increase in storminess might come about through an increased Equator-to-pole temperature difference due to global warming, as I explained above. The most well known of these indices is the North Atlantic Oscillation (NAO) index (see Chapter 4), which is based on the atmospheric pressure difference between (typically) the Azores and Iceland. A more positive NAO index means a greater north-south pressure difference, which means a greater temperature difference, which means a stormier North Atlantic. Simulations by scientists at the Tyndall Centre for Climate Change Research in the UK have recently performed simulations of a future North Atlantic, including the effects of global warming. Results suggest a systematic shift to more positive NAO-index values in the future. This will bring stronger westerly winds, bigger

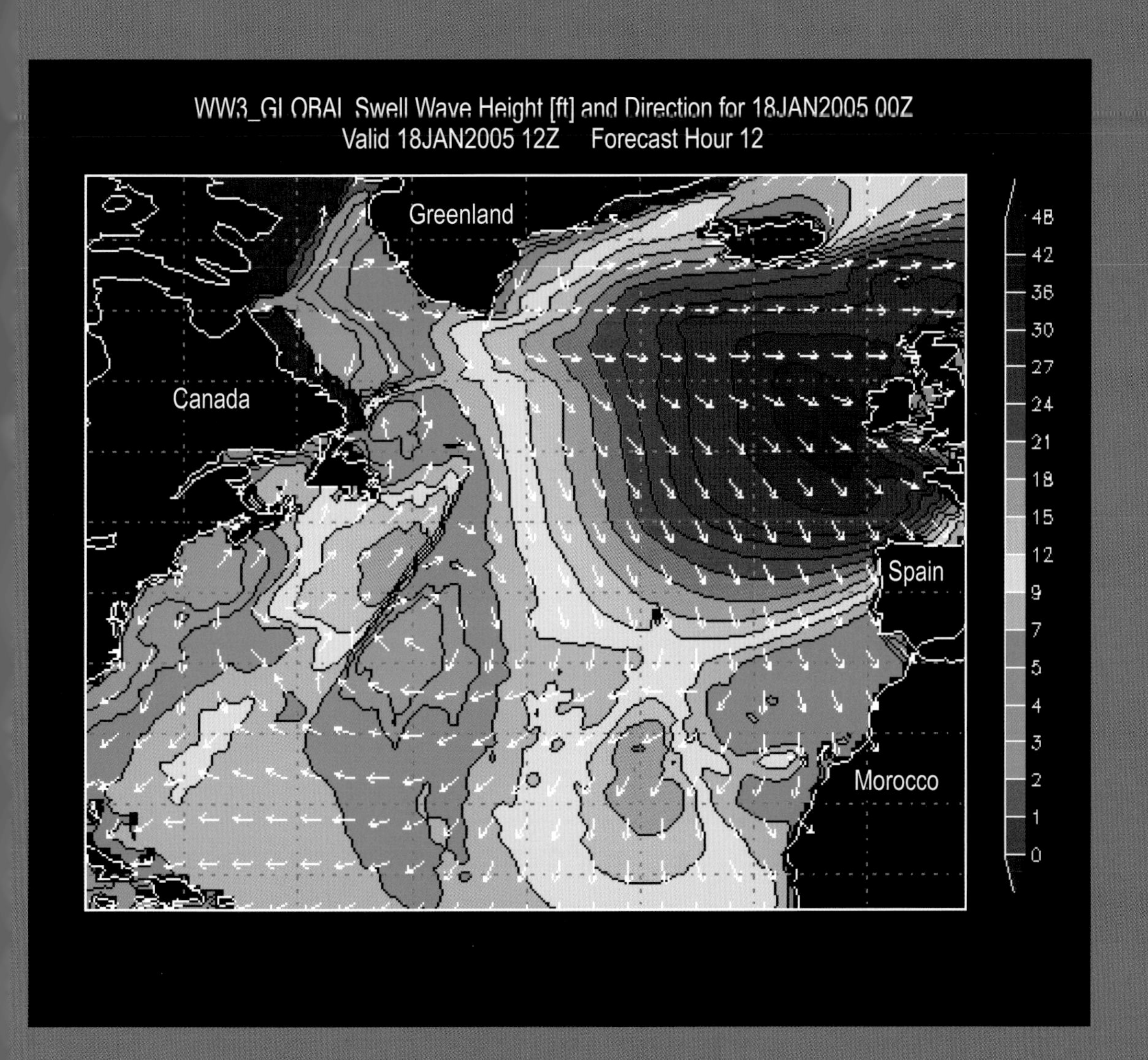

Chart showing contours of wave height in the North Atlantic for 18 January 2005. The surf at most spots in Western Europe was way out of control. Will global warming mean more swells like this?

and more frequent low-pressure systems, and a generally stormier North Atlantic. That includes, of course, bigger waves. Also, there is every reason to suspect that, if the North Atlantic gets stormier, the other oceans of the world will get stormier too, for the same reasons.

As far as surfing is concerned, does bigger and stormier always mean better? Well, not necessarily. On the one hand, the more exposed parts of the coast, already plagued with frequent out-of-control conditions, too much wind, one swell on top of another and 'too much water moving', will get worse. On the other hand, those spots situated a long way from the storm centres, or those facing away from the prevailing swell direction, might be at an advantage, especially ones that never seem to get enough swell to work properly.

In the previous chapter I pointed out that global warming will probably lead to stronger and more frequent tropical cyclones, not so much due to an increased Equator-to-pole temperature differential, but principally because of higher water temperatures. Not only will there be higher sea-surface temperatures in tropical zones, which will mean more energy for existing cyclones, but there will be larger areas where the sea-surface temperature is high enough for tropical cyclones to form (it needs to be above about 26°C). So if, in the coming decades, global warming leads to more tropical cyclones and more Atlantic hurricane seasons like 2005, what will this mean for the surf?

On the positive side, coastlines at least far enough away not to be affected by the cyclones themselves will probably benefit. The Gold Coast of Australia, which already gets great surf from cyclone swells, might end up with bigger and more consistent surf. The west coast of Europe, which sometimes receives epic autumn surf from ex-hurricanes reanimated into strong mid-latitude depressions, might end up having consistent, classic surf in places that previously had none.

On the negative side, the storms themselves might start to come dangerously close to some coastlines that were previously a safe distance away. This would cause the same problems for surfers as for other coastal dwellers who we blame for being there when they shouldn't. As I pointed out in the last chapter, one certain way to reduce the death and destruction brought about by tropical cyclones is to stop increasing the coastal population. But that means us surfers too. If more and more surfers move to coastlines that receive cyclone swells, but are also hit by the cyclones themselves, then they shouldn't complain any more than those people who complain when their luxury homes, hotels and yacht harbours get washed away.

Water quality and pollution

As the planet heats up, rainfall patterns will change. This is important, particularly because it means that, in some places, rainfall will be heavier and more unexpected. The inability of drainage systems to cope with all that sudden input of water will lead to a reduction in the cleanliness of our coastal waters, which is not good news for us surfers, or for anyone else who spends a lot of time in the sea.

There is now evidence that rainfall worldwide has been increasing, and will continue to do so as the planet warms up. But that's not the major problem; it is the nature of the precipitation, not the shear amount, which is going to cause difficulties for us. Short, highly intense bursts of rainfall are more likely to produce catastrophic floods than long periods of evenly distributed, light drizzle. Over the last century, measurements have shown a sharp increase in precipitation intensity: the rainfall has been heavier and more concentrated, but has been occurring in shorter bursts. Computer simulations suggest that this trend will continue. Not only that, but rainfall patterns over the globe will continue to become less evenly distributed, with more droughts in some places and more rain in others. In summary, the overall amount of rainfall will increase, but the spatial and temporal variation in rainfall will increase much more.

None of this is particularly good news for anyone. For us coastal dwellers, the increases in heavy downpours and local floods are what will cause us the most problems. When it rains excessively, polluted water starts to find its way into the sea. This affects us directly, since we are likely to be in the sea with it.

The polluted water finds its way into coastal waters in two ways: (a) overflow from sewerage systems that cannot cope with the increased volume; and (b) the running off of surface water from the land into the sea, dragging nasty chemicals and pollutants with it. In urban areas, for example, rainwater from people's roofs, from drains in the road and from other sources, often gets channelled into the sewers to which our toilets and sinks are connected. If the rainfall suddenly increases, all that extra water might not fit into the sewers. And when this happens, the people who control the sewerage systems often have no choice but to redirect the excess rainwater and raw sewage, all mixed up, straight into the sea.

An increase in rainfall intensity therefore means an increased chance that untreated sewage will end up in the line-up. Furthermore, when it rains so much that there is a flood, more problems start to emerge. The excess water begins to pick up all sorts of residues on its way to the sea, including pesticides and animal faeces from farmlands, oil and dirt from roads, poisonous chemicals from industrial areas, and every kind of 'nasty' imaginable from landfill-type rubbish dumps.

Extreme rainfall during the summer of 2007 caused flooding like this in many parts of southern England.

So, in the future, with global warming, we can expect more rain generally, and more intense downpours in certain areas of the world. This means that more pollution will end up in the sea. Anyone who surfs, dives or swims in coastal waters will have a greater chance of getting sick than they do now. Apart from all the other (often unknown) risks from swallowing industrial chemicals or pesticides, raw sewage contains bacteria that can cause gastroenteritis, hepatitis-A, and ear, nose and throat infections. Even if you don't get chronically sick, the prospect of surfing among condoms, tampons, faeces and bloated farm animals isn't very inviting, to say the least.

Glacial melting and sea-level rise

The rise in sea level that will accompany global warming will affect us more than most people. If the daily rise and fall of sea level due to the tides has a tremendous effect on our surf by changing the way the waves break over the sea floor, then so will a systematic rise in sea level, even if the difference is a few tens of centimetres.

First, why will an increase in the temperature of the Earth lead to an increase in the level of the sea? Two factors are involved: (a) thermal expansion of the water already in the sea, and (b) the addition of extra water into the sea from the land, due to glacial melting. Thermal expansion is already affecting a huge proportion of the water on this planet, and, although the resultant sea-level rise is pretty small, it is still very important. Because of the vastness of the oceans, a tiny rise in sea level due to thermal expansion represents an incredibly large amount of extra energy stored in the water; and this energy difference is already causing significant changes to oceanic and atmospheric circulation patterns.

The other factor, glacial melting, occurs when ice contained in glaciers and ice sheets, normally on top of the land, melts and runs down into the sea. Glacial melting has the potential to add vast amounts of extra water to the sea, and, therefore, to contribute massively to sea-level rise. The two areas of great worry are Antarctica and Greenland, where recent evidence shows much more extensive glacial melting than was previously thought. You may also hear a lot about the ice melting in the Arctic Ocean. While this is a useful indicator that global warming is real, it doesn't pose such a threat for sea-level rise because most of the ice in the Arctic is already in the sea.

Based on thermal expansion and glacial melting, the IPCC have calculated that, if we keep on burning fossil fuels and cutting down trees, the sea level could rise by almost a metre before the year 2100. There is a lot of uncertainty in the calculations; recent evidence even suggests that they might be a gross underestimation. Around the late 1990s, scientists began to become suspicious of this after comparing the measured sea-level rise over the last century with the estimated rise due to thermal expansion and glacial melting. According to the calculations, of the 1.5–2.0 mm per year measured sea-level rise, about 0.5 mm is attributable to thermal expansion, and about 0.5 mm to glacial melting, which leaves 0.5–1.0 mm unaccounted for. They concluded that either there must be something wrong with the calculations, or there are other factors making it rise. After a few more years of research, evidence started emerging that glacial melting was a lot more complicated than originally thought. The results of several recent studies suggest that the land ice on Greenland and Antarctica is melting much faster than previously expected, and may eventually become catastrophic. By examining satellite data, scientists have determined that the Greenland Ice Sheet and the West Antarctic Ice Sheet are melting at unprecedented rates: up to three times faster than previously estimated.

As far as the future is concerned, there is now worry among the scientific community that predictions of sea-level rise have been seriously underestimated. The problem is that existing computer models are inadequate to describe all the processes involved in the melting ice sheets of Greenland and Antarctica. The models assume that melting is principally controlled by the rate at which heat penetrates through the ice, but most of them don't handle very well the highly non-linear mechanisms and feedback loops that accelerate the melting. One example of this type of mechanism is the following: once the ice has gone from a particular area, that surface has a darker colour, and so its ability to reflect the Sun's radiation is reduced, resulting in more heat being absorbed. The more heat absorbed, the more the ice melts, and the more the ice melts, the more heat is absorbed, and so on. Another example is this: when meltwater drains down through crevasses it acts as a lubricant, allowing the ice to quickly become unstuck from the bedrock and slide into the sea. Scientists used to think it would take 10,000 years for melting to penetrate to the bottom of the Antarctic and Greenland Ice Sheets; now they know it can take just ten seconds.

If the worst comes to the worst and these ice sheets begin to fail massively, it will result in sea-level rises much greater than previously imagined. If the Greenland Ice Sheet completely disappears into the ocean it will result in a sea-level rise of about seven metres. If the West Antarctic Ice Sheet does the same it will mean another seven metres on top of that.

Now, assuming that global warming doesn't stop us surfing all together, how will a rise in sea level affect the waves for surfing at particular types of surf spot? The effects could be different in different parts of the world, depending on the existing coastal morphology, the types of swells, and the tidal regime in that particular area. To give a general idea, here are a few hypothetical examples (see diagrams at right and on page 150):

- A beachbreak with a fairly large, dry area of sand landward of the high-water line that never gets totally inundated even in the biggest storms. Here, things might not be too disastrous. If you are lucky, the breakpoint for a particular size wave will simply shift onshore.
- A beachbreak where the beach backs on to a cliff or road. If the beach doesn't extend landward enough to accommodate the sea-level rise, then things will be complicated. If there is a cliff or other permanent structure, the beach will not be able to readjust itself to the new water level: the waves will just bounce off the cliff without breaking. If the tidal range is large enough, there might just still be rideable waves at low tide.
- A low-tide-only reef or rivermouth break. The rise in sea level might result in the tide never getting low enough for the

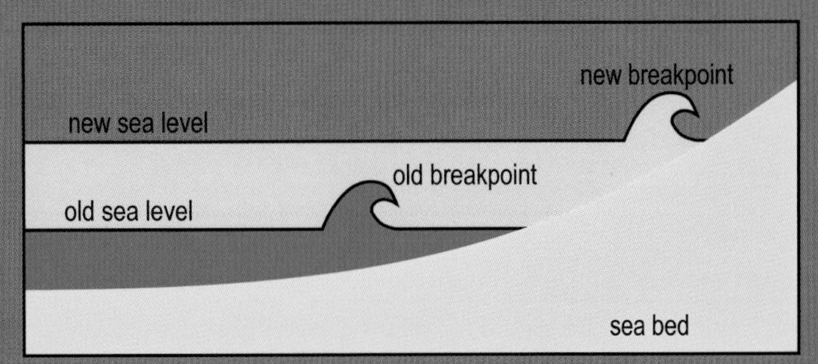

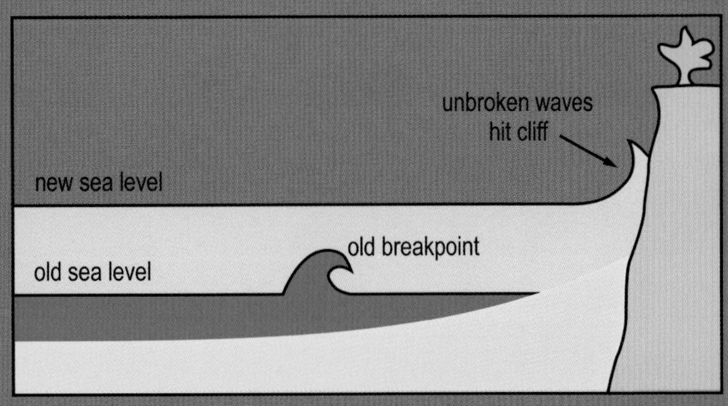

On a beach with a large enough gently sloping area inland of the high-water line (top panel), a rise in sea level might result in the breakpoint simply moving onshore for a particular wave height. However, if the beach backs on to a cliff or other hard structure (bottom panel), the water might never be shallow enough for the waves to break at all, in which case they will just bounce off the cliff.

If the beach is wide enough to accommodate a rise in sea level, waves like this could remain largely unaffected.

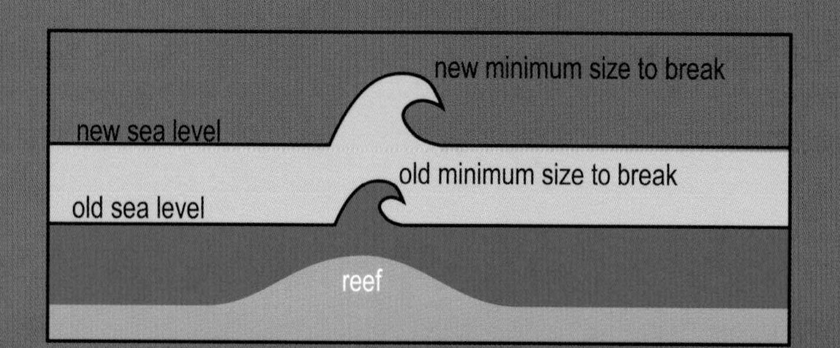

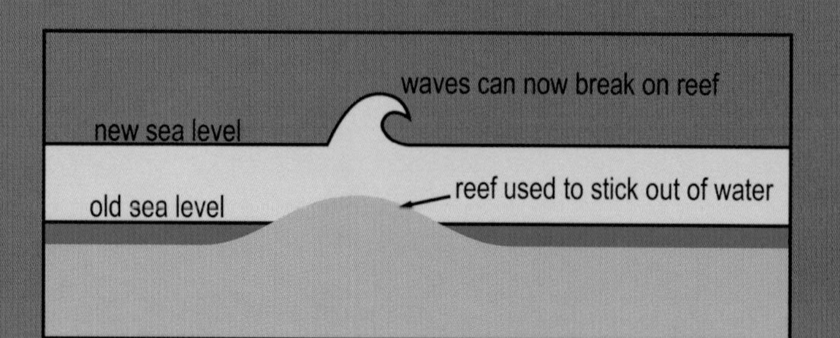

On a reef where the waves must be a certain minimum size to break (top panel), a rise in sea level will result in the minimum size being bigger, otherwise the waves won't break. However, a reef that normally sticks out of the water and hence has no rideable waves (bottom panel), might suddenly become rideable if the sea level goes up.

waves to break properly. At best, the wave might only work on the largest of swells.

- A high-tide-only reefbreak. Some big-wave spots tend to work better the higher the tide. Here, more water would be an advantage, in that it would allow bigger waves to be surfed, but then the water might get too deep at high tide on medium swells.
- A reefbreak with a very small tidal range. Here, if the waves are already perfect and you can already surf them all day, then any change in sea level will make things worse. A small rise in sea level will mean that it might only break on the bigger swells. Further rises in sea level might mean that the waves are never quite big enough to break on the reef.
- A reef that sticks out of water and/or is normally too shallow to surf. Of course, there might be plenty of reefs like this 'waiting' to be surfed; reefs which, at current sea levels, are either completely dry or just too shallow to be practicable.

Given another metre or two of water, these might become surfable.

In some parts of the world, people are taking global warming much more seriously than they are anywhere else. These are the low-lying atoll countries where civilizations have been built on coral reefs, and where most of the land is no higher than about 5 m above sea level. In two countries in particular, namely Tuvalu and The Maldives, residents are feeling the effects of rising sea levels, storms and flooding more than ever before, and many are about to abandon the islands all together. The tiny nation of Tuvalu is located in the South Pacific, just north of Fiji. The Maldives is a popular surfing destination, with crystal-clean water and picture-perfect waves, just south of India. The average land elevation in Tuvalu is about 2 m, and in The Maldives it is no more than 1 m. So a sea-level rise of 1 m by the year 2100 (which could be an underestimation if glacial melting gets out of control) would put most of both countries under water. Already, serious flooding regularly takes place when a tropical storm passes close by, or if the monsoon season brings particularly heavy rain.

The heads of state of both countries are furious at first-world nations for being the principal culprits of global warming. The prime minister of Tuvalu has stated that his country is being subjected to 'a slow and insidious form of terrorism', by countries like the USA. Meanwhile, the president of The Maldives has appealed to the United Nations to save his people from becoming 'environmental refugees'. In fact, in 2002, Tuvalu threatened to take the USA and Australia to court for excessive greenhouse-gas emissions, leading to the potential inundation of Tuvalu through global warming.

If a beach backs on to a cliff or other solid structure, a rise in sea level might cause nasty backwashes like these instead of good surfing waves.

Gulf-Stream shutdown

Finally, an important consequence of glacial melting, apart from a simple rise in sea level, is a possible shutting down of the Gulf Stream – a 'low-probability, high-impact' event that many scientists are now taking very seriously.

The Earth's oceanic circulation system helps to transfer heat from the Equator towards the poles in what has been termed the *great ocean conveyer belt*. In the conveyer belt, water is warmed up at the Equator and carried out towards the poles, where it is cooled down. In the North Atlantic, a northward-flowing surface current called the Gulf Stream brings warm, salty water from the Gulf of Mexico to the British Isles and the Northern North Sea. It then sinks, turns around and flows back again. The reason why the water in the Gulf Stream sinks when it gets to high latitudes is that it is saltier, and therefore heavier, than the water that surrounds it. It is saltier because it has come from the Equator, where the extra solar radiation has caused a lot of evaporation to take place. The name given to this kind of pattern is *thermohaline circulation* (*THC*) – 'thermo' for heat and 'haline' for salt (see diagram on page 153).

The reason the climate of the British Isles is considerably milder than it should be for its latitude, and the reason people can still surf in winter in Cornwall, Wales, Ireland, Scotland and Norway, is the fact that the Gulf Stream brings a constant supply of warm, salty water that envelops the British Isles and continues to flood into the Northern North Sea. If the Gulf Stream were suddenly cut off, or even slightly weakened, all that warm water would not reach Northern Europe, and the climate would be seriously affected. The water temperature would plummet, probably meaning that many surf spots would end up frozen in winter. Surfers in this area might therefore be some of the first people to know about a Gulf-Stream shutdown.

So, what could cause a sudden shutting off of the Gulf Stream? Well, a massive increase in freshwater run-off near the sinking points of the conveyer belt would probably do the trick. This would reduce the saltiness of the water in the conveyer belt, making it less dense, and therefore less likely to sink. If it ceased to sink, and the Gulf Stream had nowhere to go, it would slow down and eventually stop. An increase in freshwater run-off could easily be caused by the melting of the Greenland Ice Sheet – this would add trillions of tonnes of freshwater to the sea right near the sinking point of the Gulf Stream.

Just how much the run-off would have to increase before the conveyer belt no longer sank, and the Gulf Stream stopped, is not known. What we do know is that the system is very sensitive; once a critical threshold is reached, the whole thing could shut down, quickly and irreversibly. At the moment, climatic models cannot predict whether or not the expected freshwater input to the North Atlantic from the melting of the Greenland Ice Sheet will be enough to 'flip' the system. Suffice it to say that, now we know that the Greenland Ice Sheet is melting much faster than we imagined, the potential shutdown of the Gulf Stream is an event that should not be thought of as too ridiculous.

I can see that what I have just described might seem contradictory. Global warming, after all, is exactly what it says – a *warming* of the *Globe*. How can you have global warming and cooling at the same time? A Gulf-Stream shutdown cannot cause an *overall* cooling of the planet, only a cooling in certain regions – a local cooling superimposed upon a more general warming. The extra heat the planet is getting due to an increase in solar energy reaching the Earth's surface (because we are pumping extra greenhouse gases into the atmosphere) is distributed all around

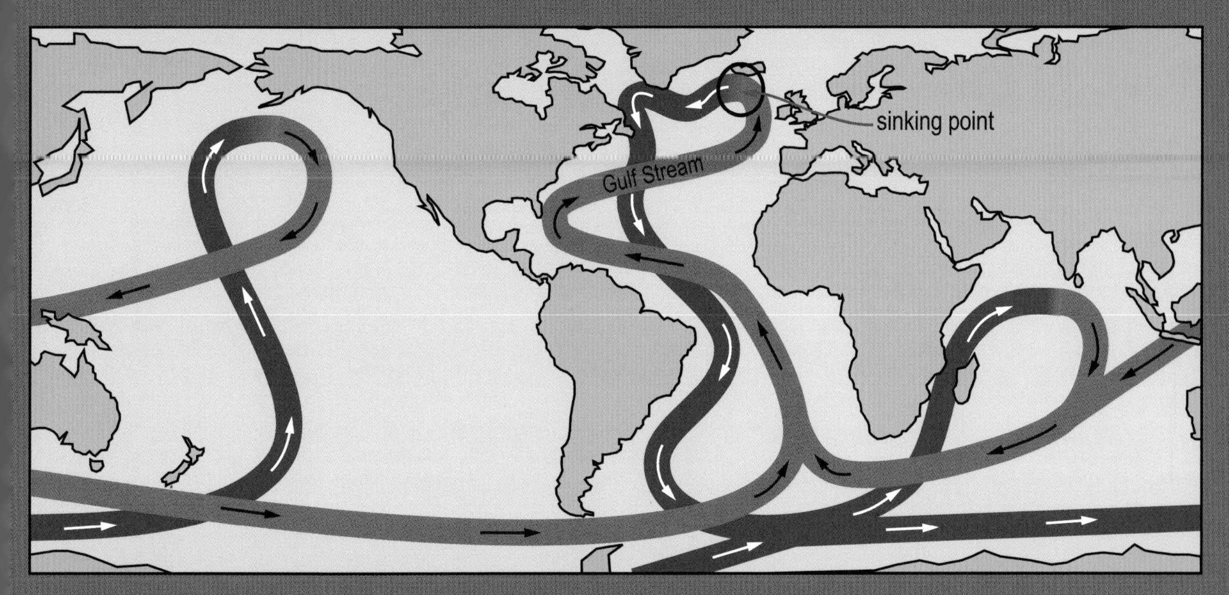

The thermohaline circulation or 'great ocean conveyer belt'. Warm surface currents are shown in red and cool deep-water currents in blue.

the globe, so the cooling of areas such as the North Atlantic will be more than compensated for by a warming in other areas.

The future

Don't get me wrong: global warming is a bad thing that we desperately need to do something about. Otherwise we'll be looking at the collapse of society as we know it, and surfing will be out of the question. However, regardless of what happens to us, the effects of global warming on surfing – particularly the effects of sea-level rise – might not actually lead to a significant reduction in the number of good surf spots on the planet. Instead of destroying them, global warming and sea-level rise will lead to a geographical re-shuffle of the world's surf spots. Changes in water level, prevailing swell height or wind regime will create as many new spots as it will destroy existing ones. Places that were once epic might suddenly become mediocre or even cease to exist, and unheard-of places might suddenly have rideable waves or even become world-class. Whether we'll be able to actually surf these places is another matter.

At best, we'll still be able to surf, but the guidebooks will have to be rewritten. Surf travel, if such a luxury is possible, will be very different. For a start, most of us won't know where to go to find good surf, and those of us who do certainly won't be able to take those short-haul weekend flights from the city to the coast, or fly half way around the world for one swell. If some sort of fuel is still available, we'll be back to living in the back of a van for six months, with a low budget and a lot of initiative.

At worst, global warming will make surfing a thing of the past – something we did when we had time to spare, when we were not struggling to find food, fighting off marauders, or caring for the sick and dying. It will be something we'll keep on thinking about – if only we'd been a little less greedy, less materialistic, consumed a little less, stopped trying to fight Nature... .

12 Tsunamis

At 00:58:53 h GMT on 26 December 2004, approximately 30 km below the Earth's surface, 250 km south-south-east of Banda Aceh, Northern Sumatra, the tension that had been gradually building up between two sections of the Earth's crust was suddenly released. The situation down there, which had been getting progressively more unbalanced, was rapidly brought back to equilibrium when a large volume of rock was displaced about 15 m. This movement was conveyed through the surrounding rock all the way up to the sea bed, into the overlying water and up to the surface of the Indian Ocean. A series of waves, each measuring less than a metre high, but hundreds of kilometres from front to back, began to radiate out in all directions. These waves didn't stop when they reached the coasts of Indonesia, Thailand, India, Sri Lanka, Malaysia, Madagascar and many other countries; they continued to force their way inland, flooding entire coastal areas, and causing a level of destruction greater than any event of this type in history. The Sumatra-Andaman Earthquake and Tsunami (which we will call the 'Indo Tsunami') was the most powerful since 1964 and, in human terms, the worst in history. The final death toll is estimated to be around 280,000, spread through 12 countries.

In this chapter I'm going to take a simplified look at some of the scientific aspects of tsunamis, with particular reference to the Indo Tsunami. First, we look at the generation, propagation and arrival at the coast of an earthquake-generated tsunami, and then I will describe a few of the most devastating tsunamis of the past. Finally, we will look at a slightly different kind of event: the landslide tsunami or 'megatsunami', which has the potential to cause coastal problems far worse than anything we've ever seen.

Many of the world's most vulnerable areas for tsunamis are right near good surfing spots. So as a surfer, particularly if you spend time in Hawaii, California, South America, Indonesia, Sri Lanka and a host of other places, you'll be interested in tsunamis. You may even have been on a coastline that experienced the effects of the Indo Tsunami. But even if you weren't, and if you don't live anywhere near a tsunami-vulnerable area, I'm sure you have wondered at some time or other what would happen if a tsunami hit.

Where does a tsunami come from?

Whether we like it or not, tsunamis are an absolutely normal and necessary part of the natural and continuous metamorphosis of our planet. Tsunamis are produced by the Earth readjusting itself to a new state of equilibrium – perhaps analogous to you or me adjusting our posture while sitting on a chair or lying in bed. These small adjustments are going on all the time, and include not only geological phenomena such as earthquakes, volcanic eruptions and ocean-island collapses, but also oceanographic and atmospheric ones such as sea breezes, thunderstorms or tropical cyclones. The particular 'readjustment' that leads to a tsunami typically consists of some shifting of rock beneath the Earth's surface. When this movement is transmitted to the ocean, the water tends to be displaced, and ends up overflowing on to any land masses that might border that ocean.

The Indo Tsunami was produced by an earthquake, so I thought it might be useful to summarize how tsunamis are commonly generated by earthquakes, and have a look at what went on beneath the Earth's surface during this particular one. Earthquakes arise due to a sudden movement of the Earth's crust, in a region where two sections of crust (tectonic plates) are trying to move in opposite directions. The two masses of rock do not simply slide over each other smoothly. Due to the considerable friction between them, they tend to get stuck together and then move in a sudden jolt. At first, while they are attempting to force each other in different directions, the stress is building up between them. Then, once the jolt occurs, that stress is relieved. Most of the time, this happens before much stress has built up, resulting in a seismic event that is practically insignificant. But sometimes the stress builds up so much that, when the jolt finally comes, a large amount of energy is released. This is when we end up with an earthquake. And if it happens below the ocean, we get a tsunami.

There are various ways in which the tectonic plates move relative to each other in tsunami-generating earthquakes, as you can see in the diagram. The *strike-slip* fault is where the plates are slipping past each other horizontally. The strike-slip can produce tsunamis, but because the plate movement is horizontal, only a small proportion of the energy discharged reaches the surface. The *dip-slip* is typical of a *subduction zone*, where two plates are moving towards each other, one of which (usually the heavier) is being forced to 'dive' underneath the other. If the majority of the movement is from the lower plate jolting downwards, then most of the energy will propagate downwards – not particularly favourable for a tsunami either. However, if the majority of the movement is from the upper plate jolting upwards over the lower one, the energy will propagate upwards towards the surface, resulting in the greatest chance of a tsunami. A movement of this type may also be termed a *thrust-dip*. The earthquake that generated the Indo Tsunami was derived from a thrust-dip. It was so big that the experts have termed it a *megathrust*.

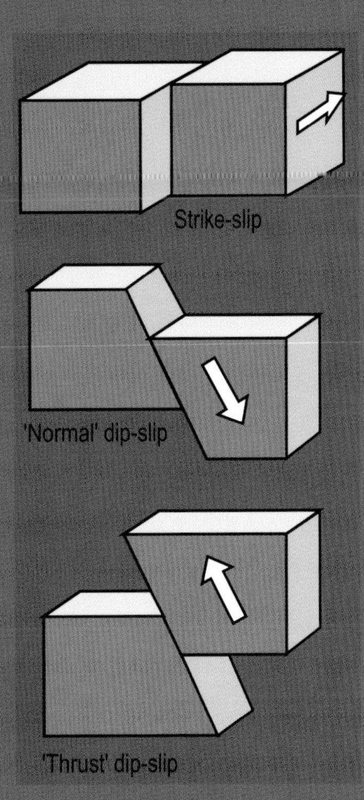

Schematic illustration showing how two tectonic plates move in relation to each other: The earthquake that produced the Indo Tsunami was the thrust dip-slip or thrust-dip, shown in the bottom diagram.

The diagram on page 156 illustrates how a tsunami can arise from a thrust-dip fault on a subduction zone. As the two plates are moving towards each other, the lower plate tries to drag the upper one down with it (a). This causes the upper plate to flex downwards and inwards, building up

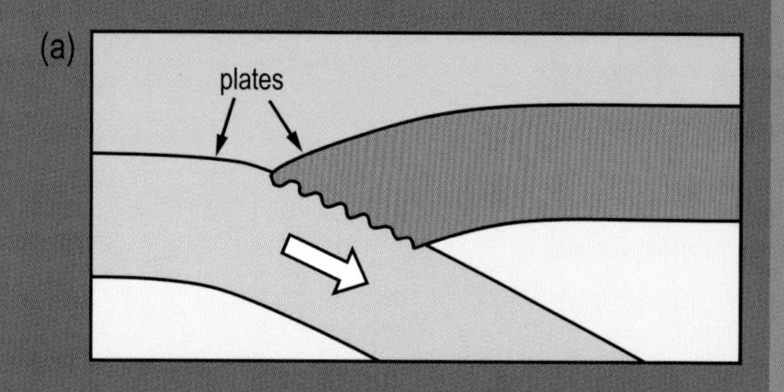

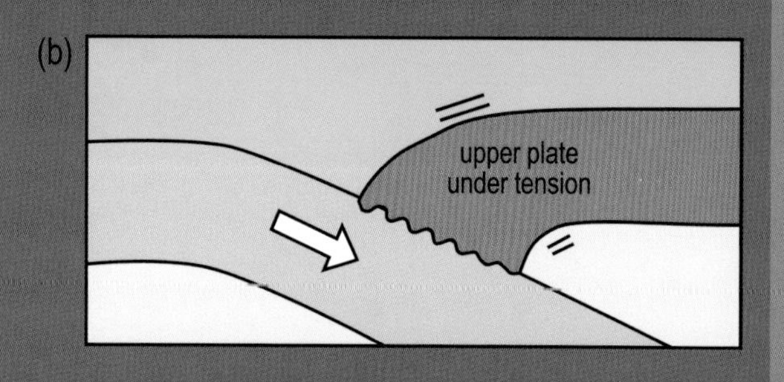

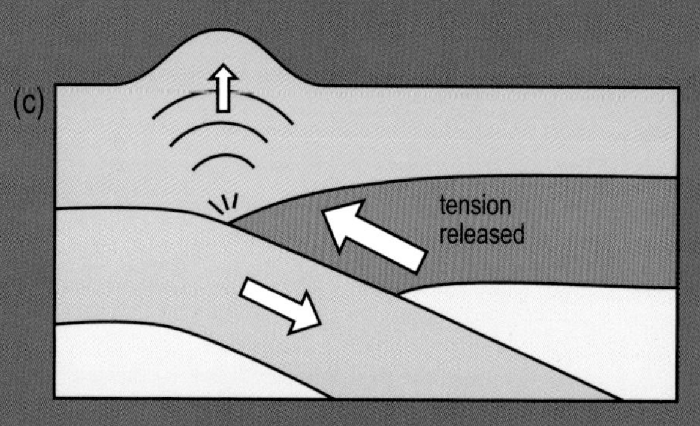

Sequence of events in a thrust-fault earthquake. The tsunami is initiated when the upper plate 'recoils', after being held under increasing tension by the lower plate.

an enormous tension inside it (b). When the friction breaks down, that tension is suddenly released and the upper plate 'springs back' to its original position (c). This movement is translated to a sudden upwards displacement of the sea bed, which then pushes the water upwards in the form of a pressure wave, quickly reaching the surface.

What results is very similar to throwing a stone into a pond, but upside down – the surface water is pushed upwards from underneath until gravity starts to bring it back down again. At this point the wave starts to propagate radially outwards.

So, what were the specific causes of the Indo Tsunami? The 'megathrust' earthquake that produced the tsunami occurred on the subduction zone between the India Plate and the Burma Plate. In the area around the epicentre, the India plate is continually undercutting the Burma Plate, which is riding on top. The India plate is trying to drag the Burma Plate down with it, which results in thrust-faulting on the plate interface. The tsunami was generated when the Burma Plate 'recoiled', resulting in a sudden uplifting of the sea bed and a shock wave which propagated to the water surface. According to estimates, the maximum displacement of the plates themselves was about 15 to 20 m. The corresponding uplift of the sea bed would have been somewhat less than this, but still of the order of several metres.

The size of a tsunami is related to (a) the type of earthquake that produced it; (b) the distance from the sea bed to the disturbance in the Earth's crust, and (c) the magnitude of the earthquake itself. The magnitude of an earthquake is commonly measured using a scale devised by Charles Richter in 1934. The important thing about the Richter magnitude (M) is that it is not simply linearly proportional to the amplitude of the seismic motions; it is logarithmic. For every increment on the Richter scale, the amplitude of the seismic motions increases by a factor of ten, and the amount of energy released increases by a factor of about 32. This explains why most earthquakes we hear about are of $M = 6$ or higher. Anything smaller would either go unnoticed or produce very little damage to man-made structures. At the high end of the scale, earthquakes become very destructive very quickly; for example, an $M = 9$ releases about 1,000 times as much energy as an $M = 7$. The earthquake that gave rise to the Indo Tsunami was about a 9.0 on the Richter scale. This, combined with the fact that it was a thrust-dip earthquake and that the fault was quite near the surface, explains why the tsunami it produced was so devastating and far reaching.

What happens after it leaves the epicentre?

After a tsunami is born, it starts radiating out across the deep ocean. It can propagate many thousands of kilometres, only stopping when it hits a land mass. Its characteristics are unique, and very different from a normal wind-generated wave. Owing to the way in which it was produced, the wavelength (distance from the front to the back) of a wind-generated wave is rarely more than 200 m. The wavelength of a tsunami, however, can be hundreds of kilometres. This fact alone has quite profound consequences. Also, closely linked to the enormously long wavelength is the speed of the tsunami as it propagates across the deep ocean. For example, the average speed of a tsunami in water depths of around 4,000 m works out at approximately 700 km per hour. Compare this with a wind-generated wave, which would be struggling to manage 50 km per hour in deep water.

Another important feature of a tsunami is that its presence in deep water is almost impossible to detect over and above all the

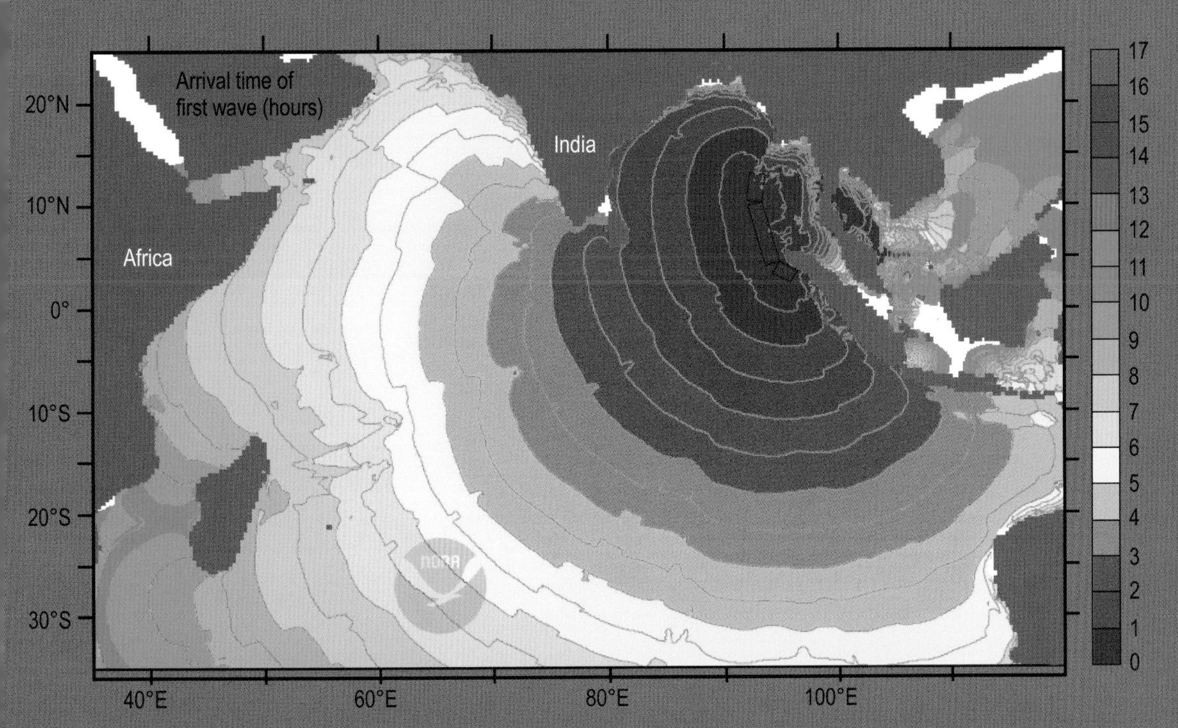

Map showing the time taken for the Indo Tsunami to spread out across the ocean. The scale on the right, corresponding to the colour contours, is time, in hours. It shows how quickly the tsunami propagated out from its epicentre. Although the tsunami hit Northern Sumatra and the Andaman Islands almost instantly, it took about two hours to reach Sri Lanka, and about eight hours to reach the west coast of Africa.

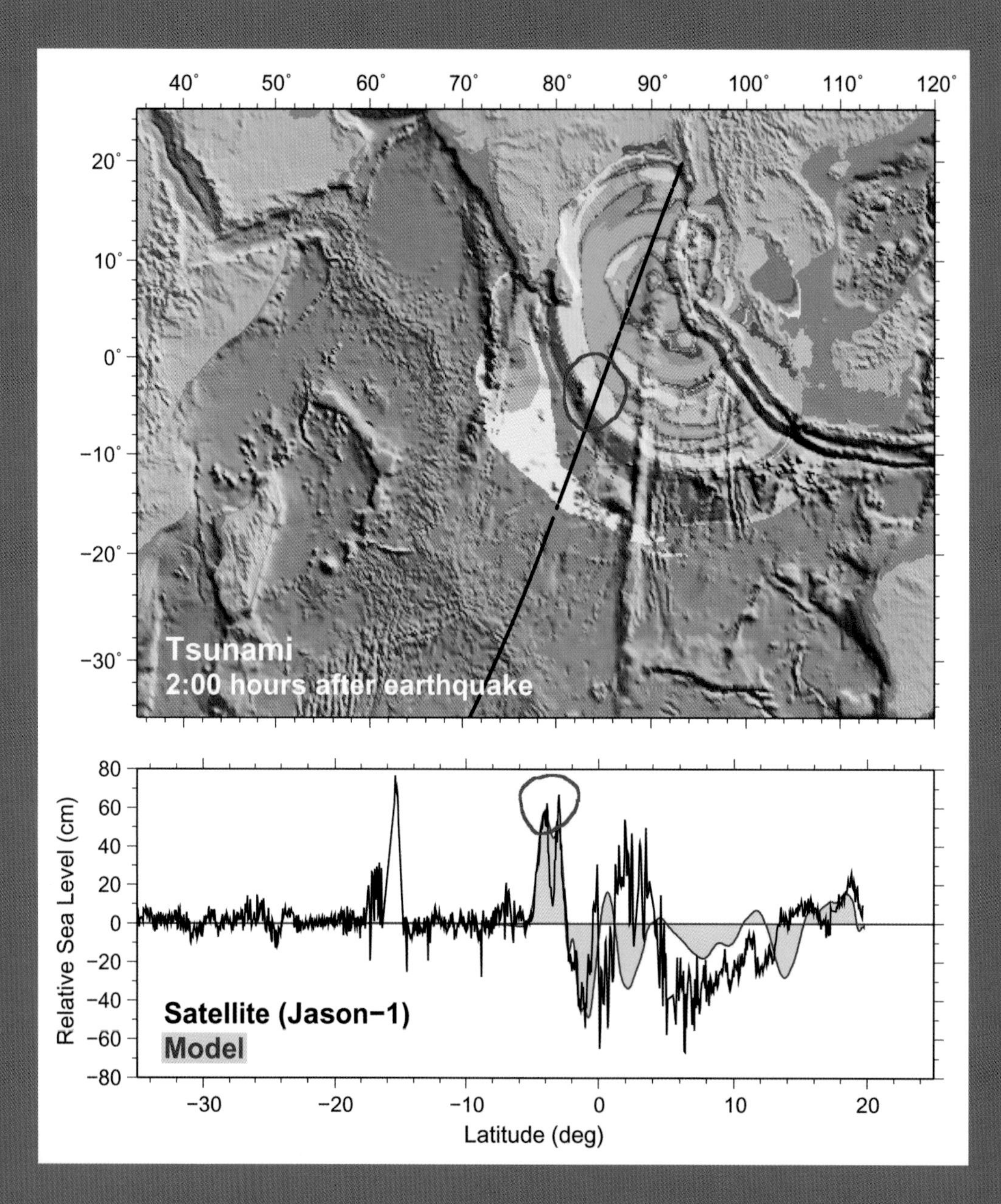

Plan view of the Indo Tsunami, two hours after it was generated. Top panel shows a snapshot of the vertical displacement of the ocean surface. The yellow contours show the peaks of the tsunami as it spreads out from the epicentre. The bottom panel shows the water surface elevation, as seen looking through the 'slice' marked by the black line in the upper panel. Note that the vertical scale is highly exaggerated. The first peak of the tsunami is ringed in red on both diagrams.

other waves. This is due to the extremely small ratio between its height and wavelength. Tsunamis are traditionally difficult to observe using satellites and other remote-sensing devices, and they cannot be felt aboard ships. Their height in deep water can actually be quite insignificant: often less than a metre, even for the most devastating ones. The diagram on page 158 illustrates the open-ocean heights of the Indo Tsunami, measured by satellite two hours after the earthquake. The graph in the lower part of the picture shows a cross-sectional 'snapshot' of the water surface along the black line in the upper picture. The peak at about 5°S, circled in red, is still only about 60 cm high in the deep water. If we count both the initial peak and the following trough, we find the peak-to-trough height of the wave is just over a metre. In the upper picture, that part of the tsunami can clearly be seen having just hit Sri Lanka. We can also appreciate that the tsunami wasn't just one single wave; it was an irregular series of ups and downs in the water surface over a great distance. The 'wavelength' is hard to determine because the thing is so irregular. However, if we just focus on that peak circled in red and its following trough, we find it corresponds to a wavelength of over 200 km.

What happens when it hits the coast?

Since the speed of a tsunami is governed by the depth of the water, it slows down as soon as it starts to propagate over the shallower water of coastal areas. As waves slow down in shallow water, they tend to be squashed up together, and so they also grow in height. This, of course, applies to any wave; but due to the enormous wavelength and speed of a tsunami, the effects are much more pronounced. Eyewitness reports put the height of the Indo Tsunami as it hit the North Coast of Sumatra at about 10–15 m. Even if the shoaling process only allows the tsunami to grow to a few metres in height when it reaches the shore, it will still contain a tremendous amount of energy. Again, because of its wavelength, a tsunami will not behave like a normal wave when it hits the coast. Instead of breaking and dissipating all its energy within a few tens of metres, it continues to propagate, ignoring the shoreline completely and forcing its way great distances inland.

Tsunamis have incredibly long periods as well as wavelengths. Compared with a normal, wind-generated wave whose period rarely exceeds about 20 seconds, the period of a tsunami can sometimes be up to an hour long. Instead of the water rushing up the beach for a few seconds and then rushing down again, it might keep on coming for half an hour before turning around and sucking everything with it back out to sea for another half an hour. The various peaks that inevitably come after the first one can arrive a long time apart.

Linked with its characteristics in deep water, and ultimately linked with the earthquake that produced it, is the *phase* of the tsunami as it arrives at the coast. The phase has to do with whether the leading edge of the tsunami contains either a trough or a peak. Many eyewitnesses tell of having been mesmerized as the whole ocean drained away in front of their eyes, like an outgoing tide speeded up a thousand times. The inevitable wall of water would start to arrive several minutes later. This initial 'drawback' is due to the leading edge of the tsunami containing a trough, which tends to suck the water offshore as the wave reaches the coast.

The magnitude and destructive force of a tsunami is often related to the maximum *run-up* at the locations where it struck land. The run-up is the vertical height on land reached by the water as it 'sloshes' up on to the land. This can be considerably more than the wave height itself. The run-up depends not only upon the height of the tsunami just before it arrives at the shore, but also on many processes related to the physical configuration of the coastline itself. The run-up can vary enormously depending on the shape of the coastline – whether it is straight or curved, or if it contains a bay or a headland.

Perhaps a more useful thing to predict than run-up height is the maximum distance inland that flooding is likely to take place after a tsunami hits the land. Scientists have come up with a very simple rule of thumb for this: the volume of inundation is approximately equal to the volume of water in the tsunami. The longer the wavelength and the higher the tsunami, the more water it will contain; therefore, the more water will end up on the land. The distance inland to which flooding takes place will depend on how flat the coastal area is and what energy-dissipating material it contains. Grassy coastal plains, for example, are not very good wave-energy absorbers, whereas pine forests are really good ones.

Large tsunamis from the past

In terms of human consequences, the Indo Tsunami was by far the biggest in history, causing more casualties than any other event of this type ever recorded. It was even worse than the tsunami caused by the famous volcanic explosion of Krakatau in 1883. The earthquake that generated the Indo Tsunami was the fourth largest since 1900, and the largest since the 1964 earthquake in Prince William Sound, Alaska. It was a truly 'global' event, with coastal damage in places such as Mozambique, South Africa and Australia, and sea-level perturbations recorded in Antarctica, New Zealand and both coasts of the Americas.

For comparison, I will list just a few of the most destructive earthquake-generated tsunamis from the past. Of course, many more tsunamis have occurred, but the ones mentioned below are the best documented, and every one significantly affected coastlines where there is good surf.

- *Lisbon, 1755:* On 1 November 1755 an earthquake of $M = 9.0$ occurred just south-west of Lisbon, Portugal. The event, known as the Great Lisbon Earthquake, has been extremely well documented,

This photo from Indonesia shows just how vulnerable many people are to coastal flooding. Any tsunami would wipe out these homes in a matter of seconds.

and has been said to have marked the beginning of serious seismological study. The earthquake itself caused severe loss of life in Lisbon itself, mostly by fire, and the ensuing tsunami propagated up the Tagus River and ended up destroying the entire city. Not only Lisbon, but the entire west coast of Portugal felt the effects of the tsunami, with water penetrating up to 2.5 km inland, and run-up heights reaching 30 m. Considerable damage was also caused in south-west Spain and Morocco. The tsunami propagated northwards, reaching the UK and Ireland, with 3-m waves being reported in Plymouth. It also radiated westwards, where waves of up to 15 m were observed on the Atlantic islands of Madeira and the Azores, and waves of about 6 m in some parts of the Caribbean. The overall death toll of the Great Lisbon Earthquake and Tsunami was about 20,000.

- *Krakatau, 1883:* The small volcanic island of Krakatau is located in the Sundra Strait between Java and Sumatra. On 27 August 1883, the volcano exploded violently. The sound of the blast was recorded an unbelievable 4,800 km away, and atmospheric disturbances were noted around the globe for up to nine days after. The energy released was equivalent to 200,000,000 tonnes of TNT, and the explosion is said to have been the loudest noise ever witnessed. The tsunami that resulted from this explosion quickly hit the nearby coasts of Java and Sumatra, producing run-ups of up to 42 m and penetrating 5 km inland. Waves of over 40 m were observed in some places. Over 5,000 boats were sunk, and the Dutch warship *Berouw* was carried 2 km inland by the tsunami. The wave propagated away into the Indian Ocean causing destruction on the coasts of India and Western Australia, and on many islands. Tide gauges as far away as the English Channel, Alaska and Japan registered sea-level changes. The death toll was over 36,000.
- *Chile, 1960:* On 22 May 1960, the largest earthquake ever recorded, at $M = 9.5$, occurred near Concepción in southern Chile. The coastline between Concepción and Chiloe Island was totally devastated by the series of tsunami waves of up to 11 m that followed, with maximum run-ups of about 25 m. In some areas, a thin layer of beach sand was deposited as far as 6 km inland. The tsunami radiated out across the Pacific Ocean, reaching Japan about 22 hours later. Many of the Pacific islands were severely affected, particularly Hawaii. The worst impact occurred at Hilo on the Big Island, where the water surged over the harbour, reaching a run-up height of 11 m and destroying much of the town. Effects were also felt in Australia, New Zealand and the west coasts of North and South America. In Japan, over 5,000 homes and many hundreds of boats were destroyed. The total death toll was estimated to be about 10,000.
- *Papua New Guinea, 1998:* On 17 July 1998 a tsunami devastated several villages on the north coast of Papua New Guinea, where the wave penetrated 4 km inland and run-up heights reached 17 m. Effects were felt as far as Hawaii and Japan, and over 2,000 people lost their

lives. This event was unusual in many ways. For a start, the cause of the tsunami is still something of a mystery. The size of the tsunami appears to have been disproportionately large for the 'small' $M = 7.1$ earthquake associated with it. Scientists are still debating whether it was the earthquake itself or some second-order effect, such as a submarine landslide, that provoked the tsunami. The Pacific Tsunami Warning Centre, which based its estimation of the tsunami directly on the earthquake itself, failed to recognize the seriousness of the event, with messages such as '*No destructive pacific-wide tsunami threat exists.*' Also, eyewitnesses report that the wave was preceded by fire and sparks; indeed, many victims did actually die from burning. What seems

This surf spot is very near 'ground zero' of the Indo Tsunami.

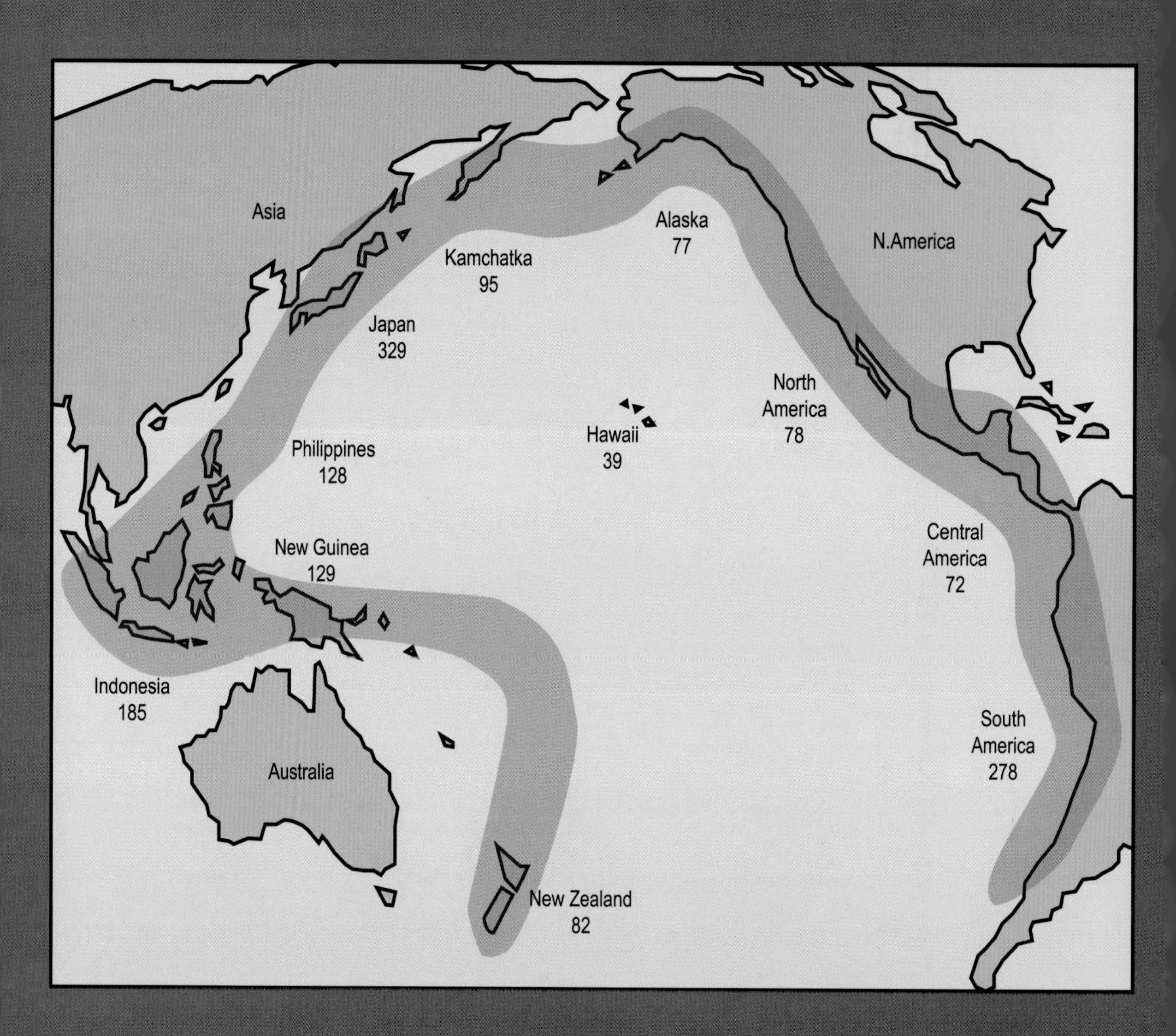

The Pacific 'Ring of Fire' (in pink), around which a great number of seismic tsunamis are generated. The numbers indicate how many tsunamis were recorded in each area between about 47 BC and 1999. You can see how many good surfing areas are affected by tsunamis, with Hawaii right in the middle of it all.

like a vision from hell of a blazing wall of water bearing down on its victims is not something conjured up in people's minds; it may have been caused by the ignition of methane gas from the Sissano Lagoon, due to the atmospheric pressure wave that came before the tsunami.

A tsunami arrives at Laie Point, Oahu,Hawaii, 9 March 1957 ...

... generated by an earthquake in the Aleutian Islands ...

... approximately 3,600 km to the north.

Not only are the epicentres of all these events very close to areas containing good surfing waves, but a large proportion of the distant coasts affected by the tsunamis also happen to be surfing areas. A good number of the world's most popular surfing destinations lie on, or very close to, plate boundaries. The entire west coast of the Americas, for example, is situated directly above a fault line. It goes without saying that the Indian Ocean sides of Java and Sumatra contain some of the best surfing waves in the world, but they are also right in the middle of one of the planet's most seismically active areas. The tsunami generated by a large earthquake in any of these areas would obviously have its most profound effects nearby, but would also seriously affect distant coasts containing surf spots. The Great Lisbon Earthquake, for example, produced a tsunami that must have had quite devastating effects on a number of surf spots in the North Atlantic (although, as far as we know, nobody was surfing in Europe in 1755). But the obvious example is Hawaii which, being in the centre of the North Pacific, is not only in a great position for receiving swells from most directions, but also receives the brunt of most tsunamis generated around the tectonically active area that borders the Pacific Ocean – the so-called 'Ring of Fire' shown in the diagram on page 164.

Megatsunami

Apart from earthquake-generated events like the Indo Tsunami, there are many other types of tsunami; but one in particular seems to have recently grabbed people's attention. It is the ocean-island-collapse landslide tsunami, popularly termed *megatsunami*. On 12 October 2000, the BBC's *Horizon* put out a documentary called *Megatsunami: Wave of Destruction*. Scientists on the programme talked about a wave of unimaginable proportions, propagating from east to west across the Atlantic Ocean. This wave would be generated by the collapse into the sea of between 200 and 500 cubic kilometres of rock from a volcano called the Cumbre Vieja, on the island of La Palma in the Canary Islands. The wave, which would have an initial height of around 600 m, would first destroy most of the Canary Islands, and then make its way across the Atlantic, where, after about eight hours, it would finish up on the east coasts of the Americas. It would hit the coast with such force that it would obliterate everything up to 20 km inland.

The Horizon documentary was based largely on scientific research done since 1994. The hypothesis of the Cumbre Vieja collapse, and subsequent megatsunami, was published in *Geophysical Research Letters* in 2001, by Steven Ward of the University of California and Simon Day of the Benfield Hazard Research Centre (BHRC) in London. The head of the BHRC is Professor Bill McGuire, natural disaster expert and author of several books on global disasters. The idea of a wave so huge, although intriguing, is quite difficult to believe, and, since the *Horizon* documentary and the publication of that paper by Ward and Day in 2001, there has been a fair amount of controversy. While McGuire, Ward and Day are absolutely convinced that this event will definitely happen, other scientists are a lot more sceptical, accusing them and their colleagues of scaremongering.

Since a famous article published in 1924 by J.G. Moore, describing volcanic material found on the sea bed around the Hawaiian Islands, geologists have known that volcanic islands are extremely unstable. They are prone to occasional catastrophic failure, sometimes resulting in enormous quantities of rock falling into the sea. These events, called *ocean island collapses*, have taken place at regular intervals throughout geological history. In the Atlantic Ocean there are a large number of active oceanic volcanoes, so the risk is high. Two of these volcanoes show a particularly worrying degree of instability. These are El Fogo in the Cape Verde Islands, and the Cumbre Vieja in the Canary Islands.

The Cumbre Vieja, reaching some 2,000 m above sea level, makes up about a third of the volume of the island of La Palma. It is the most active volcano in the Canary Islands, and one of the most active in the world, and has erupted several times in the last few centuries. The last time was in 1949, during which a large north-south fault in the middle of the mountain opened up, causing the entire western half of the island to drop about 4 m. Since then, geologists have not detected any further seismic activity, and the fault has not moved; however, all it needs is an eruption of the right magnitude and the whole mountain will be split in two. The next eruption could be the one that does it, or the next or the next; nobody knows. And the next eruption might occur next week, next year or in a few hundred years; nobody knows that either. Recent eruptions have occurred about once every 200 years on average, so it might not be very long; although small variations on the geological clock mean huge differences in time to us, so we can only tell to within margins of hundreds or thousands of years. Whatever the case, one thing is sure: with a mass of rock weighing 500,000,000,000 tonnes falling into the sea, it will be a big event.

How a megatsunami works

What is the physical mechanism behind the collapse of the Cumbre Vieja, and why are we so sure that it will coincide with an eruption? Scientists have considered various different hypotheses to explain ocean-island collapses, and the one that seems to have triumphed is the *forced-dyke injection mechanism*. This theory is based on the fact that there are two different types of rock inside the Cumbre Vieja: permeable, loose rock, and impermeable, solid rock. The impermeable rock forms a number of walls or 'dykes', between which lies the permeable rock. The permeable rock is saturated with water, amassed from years of intensive rainfalls on the mountain. Under normal circumstances, the water is contained in this permeable rock within the dykes and cannot escape. However, as soon as the volcano starts to erupt, hot magma rises up through the middle, which heats up the entire mountain including the water trapped between the dykes. As the temperature of the water rises, enormous pressures begin to build up inside the mountain. The water, now in the form of steam, will try to escape through small cracks in the rock. This reduces the stability of the mountain until a point is reached where it can no longer hold itself together. This is the point of catastrophic failure, when the north-south fault opens up and the entire western flank of the Cumbre Vieja falls into the sea. The most important implication of the forced-dyke injection theory is that it unquestionably links the eventual collapse of the Cumbre Vieja to some future eruption of the volcano.

So, what will happen when all those tonnes of rock hit the water? Without going into too much detail, it will simply produce a splash bigger than any splash imaginable. This will immediately generate a series of gigantic waves which will begin to propagate away at velocities of several hundred kilometres per hour. According to Steven Ward's computer simulation (see diagram on page 168), these waves will take about six hours to travel from 'ground zero' in the Canary Islands to the east coast of North America. Between 15 and 60 minutes after impact, the waves have already wiped out most of the Canary Islands. Sixty minutes after impact they reach the African continent. Simultaneously, an enormous wave-train is starting to spread its way up and across the Atlantic Ocean. Although these waves are up to 50 m in height, their wavelength is so long that they will probably go almost undetected by ships. (Remember that the open-ocean height of the Indo Tsunami was little more than 1 m). It is only when they approach land and begin to 'squash up' that they really start to make their presence felt. Finally, six to nine hours after impact, waves of 20–25 m in height reach the east coasts of North and South America. The important thing to point out is that these 20–25-m waves are not like normal waves; due to their enormous wavelength and velocity, they are thousands of times more powerful. According to the model, the waves from the Cumbre Vieja collapse are predicted to completely wipe out coastal communities on the American East Coast up to 20 km inland.

The debate

Now, that's all very fine – Ward and Day's hypothesis about the megatsunami was accepted and published in 2001 in the peer-reviewed journal *Geophysical Research Letters*. However, many people, including some world experts on tsunamis, think that the theory is far too speculative and should not be taken seriously. They say that volcanic islands don't just suddenly fail, and tsunamis large enough to cause destruction throughout an entire ocean basin are a figment of the imagination. The sceptics criticize Ward and Day for attempting to predict with such precision the consequences of something that hasn't yet happened. They say that their computer simulation of the Cumbre Vieja collapse should somehow have been verified with real data.

Ward and Day have been very quick to respond to the challenge, with more research and more results. They have used their model to simulate a landslide tsunami that actually occurred and is written down in the history books. On 13 March 1888, on

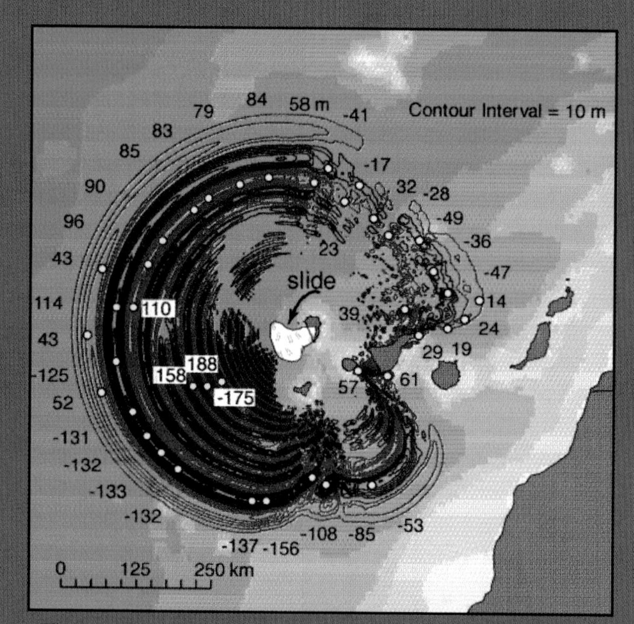

Time = 30 minutes

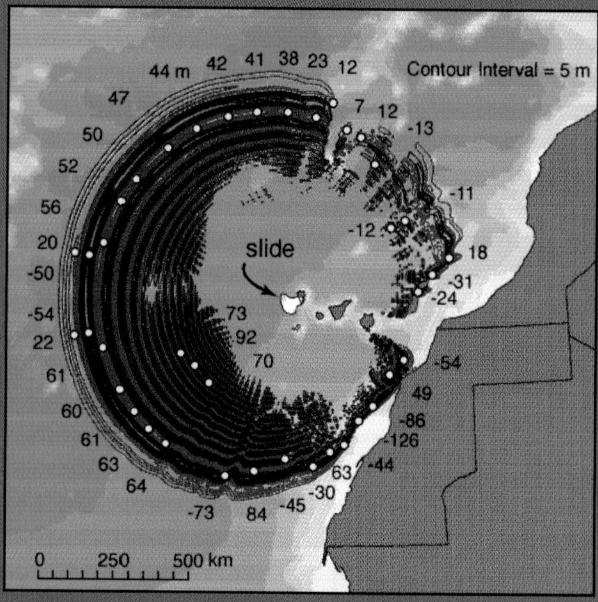

Time = 1 hour

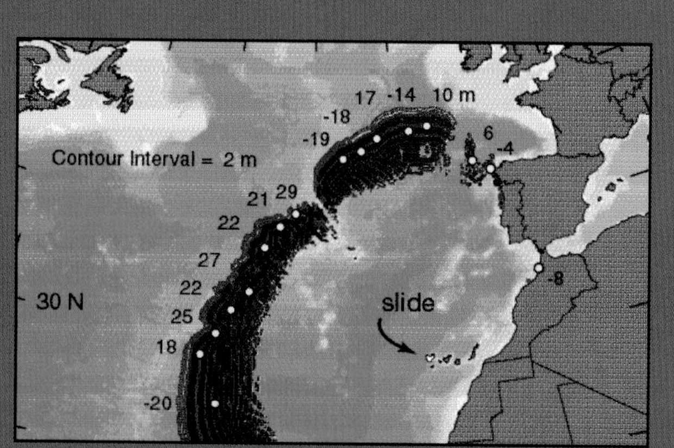

Time = 3 hours

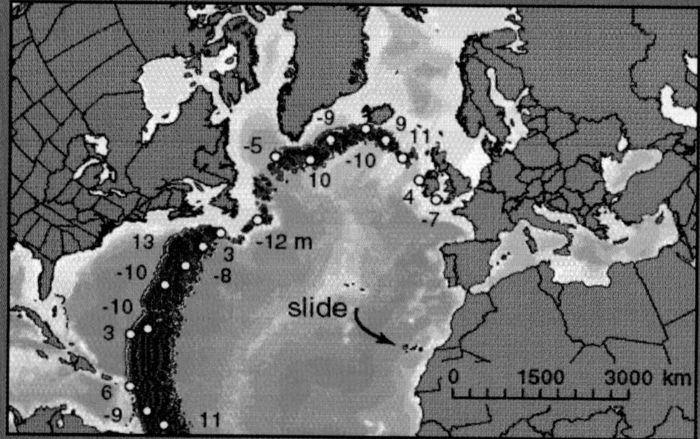

Time = 6 hours

Sequence of events after the Cumbre Vieja Collapse, according to Ward and Day's simulation. The red and blue lines are the peaks and troughs of the waves, and the numbers indicate the sea-surface displacement in metres from the average sea level. For example, 30 minutes after impact, there are 188-m peaks and 175-m troughs; when the waves reach the east coast of North America, there are 13-m peaks and 10-m troughs.

the island of Ritter, off the north-west coast of New Guinea, a chunk of rock weighing of the order of 5,000,000,000 tonnes fell into the sea, producing a tsunami tens of metres high. It caused significant damage on neighbouring islands up to several hundred kilometres away, and an estimated 3,000 people lost their lives. The difference between this study and that of the Cumbre Vieja, is that this is a simulation of something that has already happened (a *hindcast*). The model is run and the results are directly compared with the actual observed results. The observed results are not inferred from some ancient rock deposits on the sea bed or other such indirect methods; they are direct eyewitness accounts from German settlers on New Guinea. Ward and Day point out that, crucially, the witnesses had stop-watches, which means that their accounts of the incident include not only estimates of wave height but also of wave period and arrival time. Evidence including these eyewitness accounts was used to reconstruct the event, which was then compared with the version of the event predicted by the model. It turned out that the model was able to predict the outcome of the catastrophe quite well, and to the correct order of magnitude. Ward and Day consider Ritter Island a 'living laboratory', information from which can be applied to other ocean island collapses and their subsequent tsunamis, including hypothetical future events like the Cumbre Vieja.

Living with tsunamis

Tsunamis, as a form of 'natural disaster', are a little different from, say, tropical cyclones, storm-induced coastal flooding or sea-level rise, although the consequences are very similar and just as tragic, of course. The other coastal problems I've talked about in this book seem to be getting worse (or at least are predicted to get worse) due to global warming caused by the excessive emission of greenhouse gases into the atmosphere. As far as I know, with tsunamis, there is no evidence suggesting that their frequency or intensity is increasing with global warming. But that doesn't mean they are going to go away. Nor does it mean that the effects are not going to be exacerbated by coastal overpopulation.

So, what can we do about it? We know we are not physically capable of stopping earthquakes or tsunamis. To try to do this would be as stupid as interfering with the climate (see Chapter 6). Instead, scientists are learning how to predict when and where they will happen, and this should help us to figure out when to get out of the way and when not to. There is also a vast amount of research going on into early warning systems, especially since the Indo Tsunami. These systems detect the first signs of a tsunami, and then try to get the information out to as many people as possible, as fast as possible. Such a system has existed in the Pacific Ocean for a number of years, but only recently has one been put in place in the much-needed Indian Ocean. They are often based on seismic sensors, which detect the first signs of an earthquake. But, of course, not all earthquakes result in a tsunami. So, more recently, instruments have been developed to directly detect tsunamis in the open ocean – a previously difficult task due to the extreme propagation speed and the relatively small amplitude of tsunamis in deep water. These instruments take the form of highly sensitive sea-floor-mounted pressure detectors designed to detect sea-level changes as small as 1 cm in 6,000 m of water.

After the tragic consequences of the Indo Tsunami, many people are worried that a similar event might happen again. And after all the publicity about the Cumbre Vieja megatsunami, people are wondering whether that will happen too. Well, the answer is yes, of course, they will both happen. What we must realize is that these events have been occurring at regular intervals throughout geological history. They are an absolutely normal and necessary part of the natural life cycle of the planet, and they are not going to stop just because we are here. Hopefully though, the next time such an event happens, we might be able to get out of the way a bit quicker.

Some books you might enjoy

Below are a few books you might like to read to enhance your understanding of the stuff I have just skimmed the surface of. Some may be a little academic, or have the odd equation in, so I have grouped them accordingly.

Not at all academic

Diamond, Jared, 2006, *Collapse: How Societies Choose to Fail or Survive*. Penguin, London, UK. Gripping account of several cases of environmental 'foot-shooting' by past societies who have abused Nature and ended up worse off. Makes it very clear that something is very wrong in the way we are treating our planet.

Goodwin, Brian, 2007, *Nature's Due: Healing Our Fragmented Culture*. Floris Books, Edinburgh, UK. Explains how science and technology have become isolated from Nature, which is why we still think we 'own' Nature and can exploit it for our own needs. To avoid environmental self-destruction we must take a more holistic approach.

Harding, Stephan, 2006, *Animate Earth: Science, Intuition and Gaia*. Green Books, Dartington, UK. Easy-to-read but comprehensive description of James Lovelock's Gaia Theory (see below) by someone who has worked with Lovelock for many years.

Henson, Robert, 2006, *The Rough Guide to Climate Change*, Rough Guides, London, UK. The facts about global warming, just in case you wondered what it was all about. Painless descriptions, clear diagrams, and plenty of practical information.

Keeble, John, 1999, *Out of the Channel: The Exxon Valdez Oil Spill in Prince William Sound* (2nd edn), University of Washington Press, Seattle, WA, USA. Goes through in great detail what happened with the *Exxon Valdez* oil spill, and how badly managed the whole affair was. The story sounds very familiar.

Lovelock, James, 2006, *The Revenge of Gaia: Why the Earth is Fighting Back – and How We Can Still Save Humanity*, Penguin, London, UK. The theory of the Living Planet, Gaia, originally championed by Lovelock, and now almost universally accepted, applied to our recent abuse of the environment. Some great philosophy, but also some radical ideas about how to deal with global warming.

Philander, S. George, 2004, *Our Affair with El Niño: How We Transformed an Enchanting Peruvian Current into a Global Climate Hazard*, Princeton University Press, Princeton, NJ, USA. Very easy to read, and entertaining journey through meteorology, oceanography and the philosophy of modern-day science. You come out suddenly realizing how much you now know about *El Niño*, without having made the slightest effort.

Slightly academic

Bryant, Edward, 2001, *Tsunami: The Underrated Hazard*, Cambridge University

Press, Cambridge, UK. Comprehensive description of where tsunamis come from, how they work, and why they are so destructive to coastal populations. Good list of past events, although this book was written before the Indo Tsunami of 2004.

Carson, Rachel, 2000, *Silent Spring*. Penguin, London, UK, new edition. Originally written in 1962, this book is now considered essential reading for anyone interested in the environment. The message – that the lust for money and greed leads to environmental suicide – is just as relevant now as all those years ago.

Longshore, David, 2008, *Encyclopedia of Hurricanes, Typhoons, and Cyclones*, 2nd edition. Useful, up-to-date information on tropical cyclones, covering the historical, scientific and human aspects. Includes accounts of recent Atlantic hurricanes such as Wilma and Katrina.

McGuire, Bill, 1999, *Apocalypse: A Natural History of Global Disasters*, Cassell Illustrated, London, UK. Plenty of useful information about earthquakes, tsunamis and volcanoes, wrapped up in an amusing but worrying compilation of hypothetical future disasters.

Thompson, Russell, and Perry, Allen, 1997, *Applied Climatology: Principles and Practice*, Routledge, London, UK. Describes how the weather and climate of the planet affect every single part of our lives and cultures, from the buildings we design to the food we eat. Written in the 1990s, but still very useful.

Quite academic

Barry, R.G., Chorley, Richard J., and Chase, Tom, 2003, *Atmosphere, Weather and Climate* (8th edn), Routledge, Oxford, UK. Classic textbook on basic meteorology and climatology. Describes the weather and climate throughout the world, including regional differences and future trends. Not too mathematical.

Congressional Research Service, 2004, *Weather Modification: Programs, Problems, Policy, and Potential*, University Press of the Pacific, Honolulu, Hawaii. A frightening report containing everything you might want to know about this absurd activity.

Komar, Paul D., 1998, *Beach Processes and Sedimentation* (2nd edn), Prentice Hall, Upper Saddle River, NJ, USA. One of the most comprehensive reference books available on waves, beaches, coastal processes, coastal management, and everything that goes with it. Contains descriptions of much of the work done on this subject over the last century or more.

Masselink, Gerhard, and Hughes, Michael G., 2003, *Introduction to Coastal Processes and Geomorphology*, Hodder Arnold, London, UK. Modern textbook dealing with waves, tides and other processes that affect the shape and form of our coasts. A few simple equations to deal with.

Woodroffe, Colin, 2002, *Coasts: Form, Process and Evolution*, Cambridge University Press, Cambridge, UK. Comprehensive description, from a geographer's point of view, of every different type of coast, where it came from, and why it is the way it is. Good chapter on human coastal intervention.

Very academic

Holthuijsen, Leo H., 2007, *Waves in Oceanic and Coastal Waters*, Cambridge University Press, Cambridge, UK. This one is pretty mathematical, but it contains some useful material on ocean wave generation, propagation and shoaling, as well as wave climate.

Index

Acknowledgements

Photographs are reproduced by kind permission of: Wolfgang Amri/iStock, page 30; Jakue Andikoetxea, page 79; Ken Babione/iStock, pages 10–11; Henk Badenhorst/iStock, pages 46–7; John Barker, page 147; Brandon Brewer, page 118; Brandon Burgdorf, front cover; José Manuel Casal/La Voz de Galicia, page 142; Cheryl Casey/iStock, page 1; Juan Fernández, pages 6–7, 15, 17, 20, 21, 22–3, 25, 26–7, 28, 38–9, 41, 44–5, 56–7, 62, 72–3, 76–7, 84–5, 89, 95, 98–9, 101, 115, 123, 132–3, 150, 151; Gibson of Scilly, page 113; J.T. Gray/iStock, pages 4–5, 170–71; Jaap Hart/iStock, pages 86–7; Henry Helbush, page 165; Will Henry (www.savethewaves.org), pages 108, 109; HPphoto/iStock, page 2; Pablo Garitaonandia Iturrieta, page 105; NASA, pages 14, 52, 129, 138; Bernie Robinson, page 53; Tim Scott, pages 160–61, 162–3; Andrew Shields, pages 106–7; Mike Smith/iStock, pages 126–7; Martin Tullemans, pages 98–9; US Navy, page 136; Professor Chris Vincent, University of East Anglia, UK, pages 96–7; Auke Visser (www.visseraa.topcities.com), pages 74–5; Graham Walker, page 104. The photograph of the *Amoco Cadiz* on page 119 is taken from Wikepedia (http://commons.wikimedia.org).

For permission to reproduce charts and diagrams I am grateful to: Fleet Numerical and Oceanographic Center (FNMOC), pages 81, 145; Intergovernmental Panel on Climate Change (IPCC), page 141; NASA/Goddard Space Flight Center, page 64; National Centre for Atmospheric Research (NCAR), page 142; NOAA, pages 157, 158; Robert A. Rohde/Globalwarmingart.com., page 135; La Universidad del País Vasco, page 43; Steven Ward, page 168; Wetterzentrale Karlsruhe, pages 50, 51. The 555-year NAO-index reconstruction data used in the reconstruction on page 55 was obtained from: Glueck, M. and Stockton, C., 2001, *Multi-Proxy North Pacific Oscillation Reconstruction*, International Tree-Ring Data Bank, NOAA/NGDC Paleoclimatology Program. Data used to generate the charts on page 68 was obtained from the Royal Netherlands Meteorological Institute.

I would also like to thank the many people whose help and inspiration over the years have led to me being capable of writing this book, particularly Dr Paul Russell for going along with some of my strange ideas and Alex Dick-Read for allowing me to freely express them.

Published in 2009 by
Alison Hodge
2 Clarence Place, Penzance,
Cornwall TR18 2QA, UK
info@alison-hodge.co.uk www.alison-hodge.co.uk

ISBN 13 978 0 906720 58 5

British Library Cataloguing-in-Publication Data
A catalogue record for this book is available from the British Library.

Book and cover designed by Kim Laughton

Originated by BDP – Book Development & Production, Penzance, Cornwall, UK

Printed in China